WeightWatchers®

Simply Bueno!

A Word About Weight Watchers

Since 1963, Weight Watchers has grown from a handful of people to millions of enrollments annually. Today, Weight Watchers is recognized as the leading name in safe and sensible weight control. Weight Watchers members form diverse groups, from youths to senior citizens, attending meetings virtually around the globe. Weight-loss and weight-management results vary by individual, but we recommend that you attend Weight Watchers meetings to benefit from the supportive environment you'll find there and follow the comprehensive Weight Watchers program which includes food plans, an activity plan, and a thinking skills plan. For the Weight Watchers meeting nearest you, call **800-651-6000.** For information on bringing Weight Watchers to your workplace, call **800-8AT-WORK.** Also, visit us at our Web site, **WeightWatchers.com,** or look for *Weight Watchers Magazine* at your newsstand or in your meeting room.

CUCUMBER "NOODLE"
SALAD, PAGE 56

WEIGHT WATCHERS PUBLISHING GROUP

EDITORIAL DIRECTOR	**NANCY GAGLIARDI**
ART DIRECTOR	**ED MELNITSKY**
PRODUCTION MANAGER	**ALAN BIEDERMAN**
OFFICE MANAGER AND PUBLISHING ASSISTANT	**JENNY LABOY-BRACE**
FOOD EDITOR	**EILEEN RUNYAN**
EDITOR	**DEBORAH MINTCHEFF**
NUTRITION CONSULTANT	**BEA KRINKE**
PHOTOGRAPHER	**CHARLES SCHILLER**
FOOD STYLIST	**WILLIAM SMITH**
PROP STYLIST	**BETTE BLAU**
DESIGN/PRODUCTION	**LYNDA D'AMICO**
COVER DESIGN	**DANIELA HRITCU**

ON THE COVER: Mushroom and Jack Cheese Quesadillas (*POINTS*® value: *3*), page 24

About Our Recipes

We make every effort to ensure that you will have success with our recipes. For best results and for nutritional accuracy, please keep the following guidelines in mind:

● Recipes in this book have been developed for Weight Watchers members who are following either the **Core Plan** or the **Flex Plan** on the TurnAround® program. All **Core Plan** recipes are marked with our **Core Plan** recipe icon ☑. We include *POINTS*® values so you can use any of the recipes if you are following the **Flex Plan** on the program. *POINTS* values are assigned based on calories, fat (grams), and fiber (grams) provided for a serving size.

● All recipes feature approximate nutritional information; our recipes are analyzed for Calories (Cal), Total Fat (Fat), Saturated Fat (Sat Fat), Trans Fat (Trans Fat), Cholesterol (Chol), Sodium (Sod), Carbohydrates (Carb), Dietary Fiber (Fib), Protein (Prot), and Calcium (Calc).

● Nutritional information for recipes that include meat, poultry, and fish are based on cooked skinless boneless portions (unless otherwise stated), with the fat trimmed.

● We recommend that you buy lean meat and poultry, then trim it of all visible fat before cooking. When poultry is cooked with the skin on, we suggest removing the skin before eating.

● We follow the USDA guidelines for cooking meats and poultry to safe temperatures to prevent foodborne illness, but for beef and lamb (steaks, roasts, and chops) be aware that cooking them to the recommended minimum of 145°F will give you a medium-cooked steak, roast, or chop.

● Before serving, divide foods—including any vegetables, sauce, or accompaniments—into portions of equal size according to the designated number of servings per recipe.

● Any substitutions made to the ingredients will alter the "Per serving" nutritional information and may affect the **Core Plan** recipe status or the *POINTS* value.

● It is implied that all fresh fruits, vegetables, and greens in recipes should be rinsed before using.

SPICY YUCATÁN BEEF TACOS,
PAGE 71

Contents

Savory
Starters

CHAPTER 1

Homemade Flour Tortillas

1 cup all-purpose flour
2 tablespoons solid
vegetable shortening
½ teaspoon baking powder
½ teaspoon salt
6 tablespoons warm water

HANDS-ON PREP 15 MIN
COOK 20 MIN
SERVES 6

1 Put the flour, shortening, baking powder, and salt in a food processor. With the machine running, add the water through the feed tube; process just until a soft dough forms. Divide the dough into 6 pieces and shape each into a ball. Roll each ball out between sheets of plastic wrap into a 6-inch round.

2 Set a medium nonstick skillet over medium heat and heat until a drop of water sizzles in it. Reduce the heat to medium-low. Add a dough round and cook until speckled and slightly puffed, about 1½ minutes on each side. Transfer the tortilla to a plate lined with a clean kitchen towel; fold the towel over to keep the tortilla warm. Cook the remaining dough rounds to make a total of 6 tortillas, stacking them in the towel as they are cooked.

PER SERVING (1 tortilla): 114 Cal, 4 g Fat, 1 g Sat Fat, 1 g Trans Fat, 0 mg Chol, 238 mg Sod, 16 g Carb, 1 g Fib, 2 g Prot, 26 mg Calc. **POINTS** value: **2.**

✺ ZAP IT **To reheat the tortillas, wrap each one in a separate paper towel or napkin and microwave on High until heated, about 5 seconds for each tortilla.**

Homemade Corn Tortillas

1 cup masa harina
½ teaspoon salt
½ cup water

HANDS-ON PREP 15 MIN
COOK 15 MIN
SERVES 6

1 Combine the masa harina and salt in a medium bowl; stir in ¼ cup of the water, then stir in enough of the remaining ¼ cup water, 1 tablespoon at a time, to form a soft dough. Divide the dough into 6 pieces and shape each into a ball. Roll each ball out between sheets of plastic wrap into a 6-inch round.

2 Set a medium nonstick skillet over medium heat and heat until a drop of water sizzles in it. Add a dough round and cook until speckled and slightly puffed, about 1 minute on each side. Transfer the tortilla to a plate lined with a clean kitchen towel; fold the towel over to keep the tortilla warm. Cook the remaining dough rounds to make a total of 6 tortillas, stacking them in the towel as they are cooked.

PER SERVING (1 tortilla): 69 Cal, 1 g Fat, 0 g Sat Fat, 0 g Trans Fat, 0 mg Chol, 198 mg Sod, 14 g Carb, 2 g Fib, 2 g Prot, 27 mg Calc. *POINTS* value: *1.*

✸ FOOD NOTE **Masa means "dough" in Spanish, but in Mexico it has come to mean corn dough. Masa is one of the most basic ingredients in Mexican cooking. It is made by first boiling dried corn kernels in powdered lime, then washing and grinding it to a powder. Masa is a must for making tortillas and can be found in Hispanic markets and some supermarkets. Masa harina is factory-made masa.**

Homemade Tortilla Chips

1 recipe Homemade Flour Tortillas (page 10) or Homemade Corn Tortillas (page 11)

HANDS-ON PREP 5 MIN
COOK 15 MIN
SERVES 4

1 Preheat the oven to 400°F.

2 Cut the tortillas into quarters. Spray a large baking sheet with nonstick spray and place the tortilla wedges on it in a single layer. Spray the wedges lightly with nonstick spray. Bake until crunchy and browned, about 7 minutes on each side. Transfer to a rack and cool completely. Store in a zip-close plastic bag at room temperature up to 2 days.

PER SERVING (6 chips made from Homemade Corn Tortillas): 109 Cal, 2 g Fat, 0 g Sat Fat, 0 g Trans Fat, 0 mg Chol, 297 mg Sod, 22 g Carb, 3 g Fib, 3 g Prot, 41 mg Calc. *POINTS* value: *2.*

PER SERVING (6 chips made from Homemade Flour Tortillas): 176 Cal, 7 g Fat, 2 g Sat Fat, 1 g Trans Fat, 0 mg Chol, 357 mg Sod, 24 g Carb, 1 g Fib, 3 g Prot, 39 mg Calc. *POINTS* value: *4.*

✹ GOOD IDEA **Use garlic-flavored nonstick spray to add a little spice to these crunchy chips.**

HOMEMADE TORTILLA CHIPS WITH
TOMATILLO–BELL PEPPER SALSA, PAGE 15
AND TOMATO-APPLE SALSA, PAGE 14

Tomato-Apple Salsa

8 plum tomatoes
(about 1 ¼ pounds),
finely chopped

1 small onion, finely
chopped

1 small apple, peeled,
cored, and finely chopped

1 jalapeño chile pepper,
seeded and minced
(wear gloves to prevent
irritation)

¼ cup chopped fresh
cilantro

1 tablespoon grated lime
zest

½ teaspoon salt

HANDS-ON PREP 20 MIN
COOK NONE
SERVES 6

Combine the tomatoes, onion, apple, jalapeño pepper, cilantro, lime zest, and salt in a serving bowl. Serve at once or store, covered, in the refrigerator up to 2 days.

PER SERVING (½ cup): 27 Cal, 0 g Fat, 0 g Sat Fat, 0 g Trans Fat, 0 mg Chol, 201 mg Sod, 6 g Carb, 1 g Fib, 1 g Prot, 13 mg Calc. *POINTS* value: *0.*

☼ HOW WE DID IT **To get rid of the sand that clings to the cilantro, fill a bowl with cool water. Add the leaves, swish gently, and let stand about 1 minute, so the sand loosens and falls to the bottom of the bowl. Scoop out the leaves. Drain the bowl; repeat one more time. Spin the cilantro dry in a salad spinner or gently blot with paper towels.**

Tomatillo–Bell Pepper Salsa

1 (12-ounce) can whole
    tomatillos, rinsed,
    drained, and chopped
1 yellow bell pepper,
    seeded and chopped
1 medium shallot, minced
1 serrano chile pepper,
    seeded and chopped
    (wear gloves to prevent
    irritation)
1 garlic clove, minced
1 tablespoon apple-cider
    vinegar
½ teaspoon ground cumin
¼ teaspoon salt
¼ teaspoon freshly ground
    pepper

HANDS-ON PREP 10 MIN
COOK NONE
SERVES 6

Combine the tomatillos, bell pepper, shallot, serrano pepper, garlic, vinegar, cumin, salt, and ground pepper in a serving bowl. Serve at once or store, covered, in the refrigerator up to 2 days.

PER SERVING (⅓ cup): 27 Cal, 1 g Fat, 0 g Sat Fat, 0 g Trans Fat, 0 mg Chol, 150 mg Sod, 6 g Carb, 1 g Fib, 1 g Prot, 12 mg Calc. *POINTS* value: *0.*

☀ FOOD NOTE Although they look like green tomatoes, vitamin-A–rich *tomatillos* (tohm-ah-TEE-ohs) are actually more closely related to gooseberries. Fresh ones usually have their papery skins still attached. For convenience, we like to use canned tomatillos. Look for them in the ethnic food aisle in your supermarket.

Four-Ingredient Guacamole

2 Hass avocados, halved, pitted, peeled, and chopped
1 plum tomato, chopped
1 tablespoon finely chopped onion
¼ teaspoon salt

HANDS-ON PREP 10 MIN
COOK NONE
SERVES 12

Put the avocado in a medium bowl and gently mash with a fork until chunky. Stir in the tomato, onion, and salt. Serve at once or press a piece of plastic wrap directly onto the surface to prevent the guacamole from browning and refrigerate up to 3 hours.

PER SERVING (2 tablespoons): 47 Cal, 4 g Fat, 1 g Sat Fat, 0 g Trans Fat, 0 mg Chol, 51 mg Sod, 3 g Carb, 2 g Fib, 1 g Prot, 4 mg Calc. *POINTS* value: *1.*

☀ TRY IT This is a great basic guacamole that can be flavored any way you like. Stir in some minced seeded jalapeño pepper, chopped fresh cilantro, a squeeze of fresh lime juice, or a pinch of cayenne, and serve with your favorite vegetables.

Black Bean Dip with Orange and Cumin

1 (15-ounce) can black
beans, rinsed and drained
1 shallot, coarsely chopped
1 garlic clove, quartered
¼ cup chopped fresh
cilantro
1½ tablespoons sherry
vinegar
1 tablespoon grated orange
zest
1 teaspoon ground cumin
1 teaspoon dried oregano
½ teaspoon salt
¼ teaspoon freshly ground
pepper

HANDS-ON PREP 15 MIN
COOK NONE
SERVES 6

Put the beans, shallot, and garlic in a food processor
and pulse until almost smooth. Add the cilantro, vinegar,
orange zest, cumin, oregano, salt, and pepper; process
until smooth. Transfer to a serving bowl. Serve at once
or store, covered, in the refrigerator up to 4 days.

PER SERVING (⅓ cup): 74 Cal, 0 g Fat, 0 g Sat Fat, 0 g Trans Fat,
0 mg Chol, 384 mg Sod, 14 g Carb, 3 g Fib, 4 g Prot, 47 mg Calc.
POINTS value: *1.*

✺ GOOD IDEA **This dip can easily be doubled,
so you will be able to enjoy some healthful noshing
from time to time. Any number of flavorful ingredients
can be added for 0 *POINTS* value, including chopped
tomato, diced jicama, chopped orange, or chopped
apple. For the most flavor, be sure to let the dip come
to room temperature before serving.**

Red Snapper Seviche

1 pound red snapper fillet, skinned and cut into ½-inch pieces
1 cup fresh lime juice
¼ teaspoon crushed red pepper
1 large tomato, seeded and chopped
1 small red onion, finely chopped
1 tablespoon chopped fresh oregano
½ teaspoon salt
¼ teaspoon freshly ground pepper

HANDS-ON PREP 15 MIN
COOK NONE
SERVES 4

1 Combine the snapper, lime juice, and crushed red pepper in a large nonreactive bowl; mix well. Cover and refrigerate, gently stirring every 15 minutes, until the snapper turns opaque, about 1 hour.

2 Drain the snapper. Transfer to a serving bowl and discard the marinade. Add the tomato, onion, oregano, salt, and ground pepper; toss well. Serve at once.

PER SERVING (½ cup): 124 Cal, 2 g Fat, 0 g Sat Fat, 0 g Trans Fat, 60 mg Chol, 394 mg Sod, 5 g Carb, 1 g Fib, 22 g Prot, 31 mg Calc. **POINTS** value: **2.**

✸ **PLAY IT SAFE** *Seviche* **(seh-VEE-chee), a popular appetizer served throughout Latin America, consists of raw fish marinated in citrus juice. The acid in the marinade (in this case lime) "cooks" the fish, firming the flesh and turning it opaque. Since the snapper doesn't get "cooked" in the usual way, which would destroy bacteria, be sure to choose only super-fresh fish and wash your hands and cutting board with hot soapy water before you begin and when you finish chopping.**

Southwest-Style Gravlax

1 tablespoon kosher salt

1 tablespoon packed light
brown sugar

1 tablespoon granulated
sugar

1 tablespoon chili powder

1 teaspoon dried oregano

1 (2-pound) salmon fillet,
skinned

1 tablespoon liquid smoke

HANDS-ON PREP 20 MIN
COOK NONE
SERVES 12

1 Combine the kosher salt, brown sugar, granulated sugar, chili powder, and oregano in a small bowl.

2 Place the salmon, skin side down, in a large baking dish. Rub the liquid smoke into the flesh. Evenly spoon the salt mixture over the salmon, gently rubbing it into the fish with your fingers. Cover the baking dish tightly with plastic wrap and refrigerate at least 24 hours or up to 36 hours.

3 Transfer the gravlax to a cutting board; cut on the diagonal into about 24 paper-thin slices. Stored in an airtight container in the refrigerator, the gravlax will keep up to 2 days.

PER SERVING (about 2 slices): 118 Cal, 5 g Fat, 1 g Sat Fat, 0 g Trans Fat, 49 mg Chol, 449 mg Sod, 3 g Carb, 0 g Fib, 16 g Prot, 13 mg Calc. *POINTS* value: *3.*

☀ GOOD IDEA This sweet-and-smoky version of cured salmon would be perfect served on pumpernickel bread topped with a dab of honey mustard (a 1-ounce slice with 1 teaspoon mustard will increase the *POINTS* value for each serving by *2*).

TEX MEX–STYLE
CHICKEN KEBABS

Tex Mex–Style Chicken Kebabs

3 garlic cloves, minced
1 serrano chile pepper,
    seeded and minced
    (wear gloves to prevent
    irritation)
1 tablespoon Worcestershire
    sauce
1 tablespoon fresh lime
    juice
1 pound skinless boneless
    chicken breast halves,
    cut lengthwise into
    24 strips
Lime wedges, nectarine
    slices, and fresh cilantro
    sprigs, for garnish

HANDS-ON PREP 20 MIN
COOK 6 MIN
SERVES 6

1 Combine the garlic, serrano pepper, Worcestershire sauce, and lime juice in a zip-close plastic bag. Add the chicken, squeeze out the air, and seal the bag; turn to coat the chicken. Refrigerate at least 4 hours or up to 24 hours.

2 Meanwhile, soak 24 (8-inch) wooden skewers in water at least 30 minutes.

3 Spray the grill or broiler rack with nonstick spray; prepare the grill or preheat the broiler.

4 Thread 1 chicken strip onto each skewer. Cover the ends of the skewers with foil to keep them from charring. Place the skewers on the grill rack or broiler rack. Grill or broil 5 inches from the heat until cooked through, 3–3½ minutes on each side. Pile the skewers on a platter and garnish with lime wedges, nectarine slices, and cilantro springs.

PER SERVING (4 skewers): 96 Cal, 2 g Fat, 1 g Sat Fat, 0 g Trans Fat, 46 mg Chol, 56 mg Sod, 1 g Carb, 0 g Fib, 17 g Prot, 11 mg Calc. *POINTS* value: *2.*

☀ EXPRESS LANE **If you'd rather skip threading the chicken onto skewers, place them in a grill basket and set on the grill rack. Serve on a bed of chopped romaine lettuce dressed with a squeeze of zesty fresh lime juice.**

Picadillo

1 onion, chopped
1 garlic clove, minced
1 pound ground lean beef
(5% or less fat)
1 apple, peeled, cored,
and finely chopped
3 tablespoons sliced pitted
green olives
1 tablespoon chili powder
1 teaspoon cinnamon
1 teaspoon ground cumin
¼ teaspoon ground cloves
¼ cup chopped fresh
cilantro
2 tablespoons red-wine
vinegar
¼ teaspoon salt
¼ teaspoon freshly ground
pepper
8 Boston or butter
lettuce leaves

HANDS-ON PREP 15 MIN
COOK 10 MIN
SERVES 8

1 Spray a large nonstick skillet with nonstick spray and set over medium heat. Add the onion and cook, stirring occasionally, until softened, about 5 minutes. Add the garlic and cook, stirring frequently, just until fragrant, about 20 seconds. Add the beef and cook, breaking it up with a wooden spoon, until browned, about 5 minutes.

2 Stir in the apple, olives, chili powder, cinnamon, cumin, and cloves; cook, stirring frequently, until the apple softens, about 2 minutes. Add the cilantro, vinegar, salt, and pepper; cook, stirring constantly, until the vinegar evaporates, about 30 seconds. Remove the skillet from the heat and let cool slightly, about 5 minutes.

3 Spoon about 1/3 cup of the picadillo onto each lettuce leaf and serve at once.

PER SERVING (1 filled lettuce leaf): 103 Cal, 4 g Fat, 2 g Sat Fat, 0 g Trans Fat, 32 mg Chol, 158 mg Sod, 5 g Carb, 1 g Fib, 12 g Prot, 22 mg Calc. **POINTS** value: **2.**

☀ ZAP IT **If you want to make the picadillo ahead, transfer to a microwavable container, then cover and refrigerate up to 24 hours. When ready to serve, microwave on High until heated through, about 6 minutes, stirring once halfway through.**

*Add raisins
about ½ the
chile powder*

Smoked Oyster and Bean Cakes

1 (15-ounce) can black-eyed
  peas, rinsed and drained
1 small onion, coarsely
  chopped
1 teaspoon dried oregano
¼ teaspoon celery seeds
¼ teaspoon garlic powder
¼ teaspoon salt
¼ teaspoon freshly ground
  pepper
1 (3-ounce) can smoked
  oysters packed in oil,
  drained
Tomato-Apple Salsa (page
  14) or Tomatillo–Bell
  Pepper Salsa (page 15),
  optional

HANDS-ON PREP 15 MIN
COOK 10 MIN
SERVES 6

1 Put the black-eyed peas, onion, oregano, celery
seeds, garlic powder, salt, and pepper in a food
processor and puree. Add the oysters and pulse until
coarsely chopped. Shape the mixture into 12 patties,
using about 2 tablespoons of the mixture for each patty.

2 Spray a large nonstick skillet with nonstick spray and
set over medium heat. Add half of the patties and cook
until lightly browned, about 2 minutes on each side.
Transfer to a platter; keep warm. Repeat with the
remaining patties and serve with salsa, if using.

PER SERVING (2 patties): 77 Cal, 1 g Fat, 0 g Sat Fat,
0 g Trans Fat, 11 mg Chol, 259 mg Sod, 12 g Carb, 3 g Fib,
5 g Prot, 28 mg Calc. *POINTS* value: *1.*

✺ HOW WE DID IT These savory bites are
crispy on the outside and meltingly soft on the
inside. For the best results, don't shape them into
patties larger than we recommend, or they may fall
apart when turned.

Mushroom and Jack Cheese Quesadillas

½ **pound fresh white or cremini mushrooms, sliced**

1 **teaspoon dried oregano**

½ **teaspoon freshly ground pepper**

8 **(8-inch) fat-free whole-wheat flour tortillas**

8 **tablespoons shredded Monterey Jack cheese**

8 **tablespoons prepared chipotle chile salsa**

HANDS-ON PREP 10 MIN
COOK 20 MIN
SERVES 8

1 Spray a large nonstick skillet with nonstick spray and set over medium heat. Add the mushrooms and cook, stirring occasionally, until they give off their liquid and it reduces to a glaze, about 6 minutes. Stir in the oregano and pepper; cook, stirring constantly, just until fragrant, about 15 seconds. Remove the skillet from the heat.

2 Place 4 of the tortillas on a work surface. Top each with 1 tablespoon of the cheese, one-quarter of the mushroom mixture, and 1 tablespoon of the remaining cheese. Top with the remaining 4 tortillas, lightly pressing down to flatten slightly.

3 Wipe the skillet clean with a paper towel. Spray with nonstick spray and set over medium heat. Add 1 of the quesadillas and cook until crisp and the cheese begins to melt, about 1½ minutes on each side. Transfer to a cutting board and cover loosely with foil to keep warm. Cook the remaining 3 quesadillas. Cut each quesadilla into 4 wedges, making a total of 16 wedges. Serve with the salsa.

PER SERVING (2 wedges and 1 tablespoon salsa): 171 Cal, 3 g Fat, 1 g Sat Fat, 0 g Trans Fat, 6 mg Chol, 349 mg Sod, 31 g Carb, 5 g Fib, 8 g Prot, 119 mg Calc. *POINTS* value: *3.*

☀ FOOD NOTE **We love the smoky heat the chipotle salsa adds to these cheese quesadillas. Chipotle chiles, which are smoked jalapeño peppers, are on the fiery side, so if you prefer, use your favorite mild salsa instead.**

MUSHROOM AND JACK CHEESE QUESADILLAS WITH LIMEADE, PAGE 217

Santa Fe–Style Pumpkin Seeds

2 cups shelled pumpkin
  seeds (about 10 ounces)
2 teaspoons Worcestershire
  sauce
1 teaspoon liquid smoke
1 teaspoon ground cumin
1 teaspoon ancho chili
  powder
½ teaspoon garlic powder
½ teaspoon paprika
¼ teaspoon cinnamon
⅛ teaspoon cayenne
  (optional)

HANDS-ON PREP 10 MIN
COOK 15 MIN
SERVES 32

1 Preheat the oven to 325°F. Line a large baking sheet with parchment paper.

2 Combine the pumpkin seeds, Worcestershire sauce, and liquid smoke in a large bowl; toss to coat. Combine the remaining ingredients in a small bowl. Sprinkle over the pumpkin seeds; stir vigorously with a wooden spoon to evenly coat.

3 Spread the seeds out on the baking sheet. Bake, stirring twice, until dried and lightly browned, about 15 minutes. Let cool on the baking sheet on a rack about 30 minutes. Serve at once or store in a zip-close plastic bag up to 1 month.

PER SERVING (1 tablespoon): 76 Cal, 6 g Fat, 1 g Sat Fat, 0 g Trans Fat, 0 mg Chol, 8 mg Sod, 2 g Carb, 1 g Fib, 5 g Prot, 8 mg Calc. **POINTS** value: **2.**

⚙ TRY IT Pumpkin seeds, *pepitas* (peh-PEE-tahs) in Spanish, are a Southwestern tradition. They're often served before dinner as a spicy accompaniment to fresh fruit-juice punch. You can find shelled green pumpkin seeds in health-food stores.

Best-Ever Gazpacho

2 ripe tomatoes, coarsely
   chopped
1 green bell pepper, seeded
   and coarsely chopped
¼ seedless cucumber,
   cut into chunks
1 small red onion, coarsely
   chopped
2 slices rustic bread, torn
   into pieces (about 1 cup)
1 tablespoon olive oil
2 garlic cloves, minced
2 cups tomato juice
1 (14½-ounce) can
   vegetable broth
¼ cup fresh lemon juice
¼ teaspoon freshly ground
   pepper

HANDS-ON PREP 25 MIN
COOKS NONE
SERVES 4

1 Finely chop ¼ cup each of the tomato, bell pepper, cucumber, and red onion. Combine the vegetables in a small bowl; cover and set aside in the refrigerator.

2 Put the remaining tomato, bell pepper, cucumber, and red onion in a food processor. Add the bread, oil, and garlic; pulse until a very coarse puree.

3 Transfer the mixture to a large bowl; stir in the remaining ingredients. Cover and refrigerate until well chilled, at least 2 hours or up to 2 days. Ladle the gazpacho into 4 chilled bowls and top with the reserved chopped vegetables.

PER SERVING (1½ cups soup and ¼ cup vegetable topping): 121 Cal, 4 g Fat, 1 g Sat Fat, 0 g Trans Fat, 0 mg Chol, 903 mg Sod, 20 g Carb, 3 g Fib, 3 g Prot, 45 mg Calc. *POINTS* value: *2.*

✸ GOOD IDEA **In Spain, gazpacho is often served as a smooth and silky pureed soup. Ours is chunky-smooth, but for a change of pace, you can puree the vegetables in the food processor a little longer, until very smooth.**

Simply Soup

CHAPTER 2

TORTILLA, BEEF, AND
BEAN SOUP

Tortilla, Beef, and Bean Soup

2 teaspoons canola oil
½ pound ground lean beef
   (7% or less fat)
1 onion, chopped
2 garlic cloves, minced
2 teaspoons ancho chile
   powder
4 cups reduced-sodium
   beef broth
1 (14½-ounce) can diced
   tomatoes with green
   pepper, celery, and
   onions
2 (15-ounce) cans red
   kidney beans, rinsed
   and drained
¼ cup fresh cilantro leaves
¼ cup shredded reduced-fat
   cheddar cheese
8 baked tortilla chips,
   coarsely broken

HANDS-ON PREP 10 MIN
COOK 15 MIN
SERVES 4

1 Heat the oil in a nonstick Dutch oven over medium-high heat. Add the ground beef and cook, breaking it up with a wooden spoon, until browned, about 3 minutes. Add the onion, garlic, and chile powder. Cook, stirring frequently, until softened, about 3 minutes.

2 Add the broth, tomatoes, and beans to the Dutch oven; bring to a boil. Reduce the heat and simmer about 5 minutes. Just before serving, stir in the cilantro. Ladle the soup into 4 bowls and sprinkle with the cheese and tortilla chips.

PER SERVING (2 cups soup, 2 tortilla chips, and 1 tablespoon cheese): 390 Cal, 9 g Fat, 3 g Sat Fat, 0 g Trans Fat, 33 mg Chol, 938 mg Sod, 49 g Carb, 11 g Fib, 32 g Prot, 155 mg Calc. *POINTS* value: **8.**

✺ GOOD IDEA **If you like, make the tortilla-chip garnish for this soup special by using homemade tortilla chips. Follow our recipe on page 12, but instead of cutting the tortillas into quarters, use a sharp knife to cut them into dramatic long, thin triangles.**

Spicy Pork, Sweet Potato, and Plantain Bowl

1 teaspoon canola oil

1 pound boneless pork loin, trimmed and cut into ½-inch cubes

1 onion, chopped

1 green or yellow bell pepper, chopped

2 teaspoons chipotle chile powder

¾ teaspoon salt

⅛ teaspoon cinnamon

4 cups reduced-sodium chicken broth

1 large sweet potato, peeled and cut into ½-inch dice

2 ripe plantains or bananas, cut into 1-inch chunks

2 tablespoons cornmeal

HANDS-ON PREP 15 MIN
COOK 50 MIN
SERVES 4

1 Heat the oil in a nonstick Dutch oven over medium-high heat. Add the pork and cook, turning occasionally, until lightly browned, about 5 minutes. Transfer the pork to a plate and set aside.

2 Add the onion and bell pepper to the Dutch oven; cook, stirring occasionally, until softened, about 3 minutes. Stir in the chile powder, salt, and cinnamon; cook, stirring constantly, until fragrant, about 1 minute. Return the pork to the Dutch oven and stir in the broth; bring to a boil. Reduce the heat and simmer, covered, about 20 minutes. Add the potato and simmer, covered, stirring occasionally, until the pork and potato are tender, about 15 minutes.

3 Add the plantains to the Dutch oven and cook about 2 minutes. Sprinkle in the cornmeal and cook, stirring constantly, until the mixture is slightly thickened, 2–3 minutes.

PER SERVING (1½ cups): 430 Cal, 11 g Fat, 3 g Sat Fat, 0 g Trans Fat, 72 mg Chol, 1076 mg Sod, 56 g Carb, 6 g Fib, 31 g Prot, 57 mg Calc. **POINTS** value: **9.**

✿ GOOD IDEA **This one-bowl entrée is chock full of flavor. We suggest beginning the meal with a generous portion of mixed greens dressed with a sprinkling of white balsamic vinegar, salt, and pepper.**

Chicken-Rice Soup with Cumin Cream

5 cups reduced-sodium chicken broth

4 (½-pound) whole chicken legs, skinned

⅓ cup brown rice

1 large carrot, chopped

½ cup diced jicama or celery

2 garlic cloves, minced

2 jalapeño chile peppers, seeded and chopped (wear gloves to prevent irritation)

2 tomatoes, chopped

¼ cup fat-free sour cream

1 teaspoon ground cumin

3 scallions, thinly sliced on diagonal

¼ cup chopped fresh cilantro or parsley

HANDS-ON PREP 20 MIN
COOK 50 MIN
SERVES 4

1 Bring the broth to a boil in a Dutch oven. Add the chicken legs, rice, carrot, jicama, garlic, and jalapeño pepper; return to a boil. Reduce the heat and simmer until the chicken is cooked through and the rice has absorbed the liquid and is tender, about 35 minutes.

2 Transfer the chicken to a plate. When cool enough to handle, shred the chicken; discard the bones. Return the chicken to the soup and stir in the tomatoes; bring to a boil. Reduce the heat and simmer about 2 minutes.

3 Meanwhile, combine the sour cream and cumin in a small bowl.

4 Ladle the soup into 4 bowls and sprinkle with the scallions and cilantro. Garnish each serving with a drizzle of the cumin cream.

PER SERVING (1¾ cups soup and 1 tablespoon cumin cream): 297 Cal, 8 g Fat, 3 g Sat Fat, 0 g Trans Fat, 84 mg Chol, 811 mg Sod, 21 g Carb, 3 g Fib, 35 g Prot, 100 mg Calc. *POINTS* value: **6.**

✺ HOW WE DID IT **For really fresh cumin flavor, we recommend toasting and grinding your own cumin seeds. Here's how: Toast about 2 tablespoons of cumin seeds in a small dry skillet over medium heat, tossing them often, until fragrant, 3–4 minutes. Transfer the seeds to a plate to cool, then grind them in a spice grinder or coffee grinder. Store any leftovers in a small covered jar.**

Turkey Posole with Radish-Scallion Topping

2 teaspoons canola oil

1 pound ground skinless turkey breast

1 onion, chopped

2 garlic cloves, minced

3 cups reduced-sodium chicken broth

1 (15-ounce) can hominy, drained

1 (14½-ounce) can Mexican-style tomatoes

1 tablespoon chopped chipotle en adobo

2 teaspoons dried oregano

4 radishes, finely chopped

3 scallions, thinly sliced on diagonal

3 tablespoons shredded reduced-fat cheddar cheese

HANDS-ON PREP 20 MIN
COOK 33 MIN
SERVES 4

1 Heat 1 teaspoon of the oil in a nonstick Dutch oven over medium-high heat. Add the turkey and cook, breaking it up with a spoon, until browned, about 6 minutes. Transfer to a medium bowl and set aside.

2 Add the remaining 1 teaspoon oil to the Dutch oven. Add the onion and garlic; cook over medium heat, stirring occasionally, until golden, about 6 minutes. Return the turkey to the Dutch oven. Stir in the broth, hominy, tomatoes, chipotle en adobo, and oregano; bring to a boil. Reduce the heat and simmer, partially covered, until the flavors are blended, about 15 minutes.

3 Combine the radishes, scallions, and cheese in a small bowl; sprinkle over the posole.

PER SERVING (1¾ cups posole and 2 tablespoons topping): 277 Cal, 6 g Fat, 1 g Sat Fat, 0 g Trans Fat, 76 mg Chol, 1224 mg Sod, 21 g Carb, 4 g Fib, 34 g Prot, 125 mg Calc. *POINTS* value: **5.**

✸ FOOD NOTE *Posole* (poh-SOH-lay) is a hearty Mexican soup usually consisting of meat or poultry, broth, hominy, vegetables, and spices. Hominy, which is available white or yellow, is made from lime-treated corn kernels. It is found in supermarkets in the ethnic food aisle or near the canned beans.

**TURKEY POSOLE WITH
RADISH-SCALLION TOPPING**

Southwest Chicken, Bean, and Corn Soup

2 teaspoons canola oil

1 large onion, chopped

3 garlic cloves, minced

2 teaspoons chipotle chile powder

4 cups reduced-sodium chicken broth

1 (15-ounce) can pinto beans, rinsed and drained

1 (14½-ounce) can diced tomatoes

2 ears corn, each cut into 4 pieces

2 cups chopped cooked chicken

2 teaspoons fresh lime juice

2 tablespoons chopped fresh cilantro

HANDS-ON PREP 15 MIN
COOK 20 MIN
SERVES 4

1 Heat the oil in a nonstick Dutch oven over medium heat. Add the onion and garlic; cook, stirring frequently, until golden, about 6 minutes. Add the chile powder and cook, stirring constantly, until fragrant, about 30 seconds.

2 Add the broth, beans, tomatoes, and corn to the Dutch oven; bring to a boil. Reduce the heat and simmer about 5 minutes. Add the chicken and lime juice; cook, stirring occasionally, until heated through, about 3 minutes. Serve sprinkled with the cilantro.

PER SERVING (generous 2 cups): 361 Cal, 9 g Fat, 2 g Sat Fat, 0 g Trans Fat, 60 mg Chol, 882 mg Sod, 41 g Carb, 10 g Fib, 33 g Prot, 109 mg Calc. *POINTS* value: *7.*

✳ **EXPRESS LANE** Save time by buying a supermarket or deli rotisserie chicken for this soup. Remove the skin and chop enough of the meat to equal 2 cups. Enjoy any remaining chicken in a sandwich on whole-grain bread with thick slices of tomato, crisp lettuce, and a touch of Dijon mustard.

Brazilian Black Bean and Chorizo Soup

¼ pound chorizo sausage,
  casings removed and
  sausage chopped
1 onion, chopped
2 garlic cloves, minced
¼ teaspoon crushed red
  pepper
3 cups reduced-sodium
  chicken broth
3 (15½-ounce) cans black
  beans, rinsed and drained
¼ cup chopped fresh
  cilantro
2 teaspoons grated
  orange zest

HANDS-ON PREP 15 MIN
COOK 15 MIN
SERVES 6

1 Spray a nonstick Dutch oven with nonstick spray and set over medium-high heat. Add the sausage, onion, garlic, and crushed red pepper; cook, stirring frequently, until the sausage is browned and cooked through, about 7 minutes.

2 Add the broth and beans to the Dutch oven; bring to a boil. Reduce the heat and simmer about 5 minutes. Just before serving, sprinkle with the cilantro and orange zest.

PER SERVING (scant 1¼ cups): 317 Cal, 8 g Fat, 3 g Sat Fat, 0 g Trans Fat, 17 mg Chol, 1087 mg Sod, 43 g Carb, 10 g Fib, 19 g Prot, 123 mg Calc. **POINTS** value: **6.**

☀ FOOD NOTE Chorizo sausage is smoked pork sausage that is highly seasoned with cayenne, garlic, and paprika. It is popular in both Mexican and Spanish cooking and is available in specialty food stores. If you can't find it, use good-quality hot Italian sausage links instead.

MEXICAN SEAFOOD
CHOWDER

Mexican Seafood Chowder

1 tablespoon olive oil
1 large onion, chopped
3 garlic cloves, minced
1 teaspoon dried oregano
¼ teaspoon cinnamon
1 red bell pepper, seeded
   and chopped
2 tablespoons whole-wheat
   flour
4 cups fish or vegetable
   broth or bottled clam
   juice
2 (14½-ounce) cans diced
   tomatoes with jalapeños
3 cups fresh or frozen
   corn kernels
1½ pounds tilapia or halibut
   fillets, cut into 1-inch
   pieces
1 pound large shrimp,
   peeled and deveined
⅓ cup chopped fresh
   cilantro
1 lime, cut into 6 wedges

HANDS-ON PREP 20 MIN
COOK 20 MIN
SERVES 6

1 Heat the oil in a nonstick Dutch oven over medium-high heat. Add the onion, garlic, oregano, and cinnamon; cook, stirring frequently, until softened, about 3 minutes.

2 Add the bell pepper to the Dutch oven and cook, stirring frequently, until softened, about 2 minutes. Add the flour and cook, stirring constantly, until lightly browned, about 1 minute. Gradually stir in the broth, then add the tomatoes and corn. Cook, stirring occasionally, until the soup bubbles and thickens slightly, about 5 minutes.

3 Add the tilapia and shrimp to the Dutch oven; bring the soup to a simmer. Cook until the fish is just opaque in the center, about 4 minutes. Stir in the cilantro and serve with the lime wedges.

PER SERVING (2 cups): 276 Cal, 5 g Fat, 1 g Sat Fat, 0 g Trans Fat, 136 mg Chol, 697 mg Sod, 27 g Carb, 5 g Fib, 34 g Prot, 113 mg Calc. **POINTS** value: **5.**

☀ MAKE IT CORE Omit the flour. This will make the chowder a bit thinner, so use only 3 cups broth.

Tortilla-Lime Soup

1 teaspoon olive oil
1 onion, chopped
2 garlic cloves, minced
2 teaspoons ground cumin
⅛ teaspoon cayenne
4 cups vegetable broth
1 (14½-ounce) can
  Mexican-style stewed
  tomatoes
2 cups fresh or frozen
  corn kernels
2 (6-inch) corn tortillas, cut
  into 2 x ½-inch strips
2 tablespoons fresh lime
  juice
⅓ cup packed fresh
  cilantro leaves
½ Hass avocado, pitted,
  peeled, and diced

HANDS-ON PREP 12 MIN
COOK 18 MIN
SERVES 4

1 Heat the oil in a large nonstick Dutch oven over medium-high heat. Add the onion and garlic; cook, stirring frequently, until golden, about 6 minutes. Add the cumin and cayenne; cook, stirring constantly, until fragrant, about 30 seconds.

2 Add the broth, tomatoes, and corn to the Dutch oven; bring to a boil. Reduce the heat and simmer about 5 minutes.

3 Meanwhile, spray a large nonstick skillet with nonstick spray and set over medium-high heat. Add the tortilla strips and cook, turning occasionally, until crisp and golden, about 4 minutes.

4 Remove the soup from the heat; stir in the lime juice and cilantro. Ladle the soup into 4 bowls and top with the tortilla strips and avocado.

PER SERVING (generous 2 cups): 180 Cal, 6 g Fat, 1 g Sat Fat, 0 g Trans Fat, 0 mg Chol, 1157 mg Sod, 33 g Carb, 6 g Fib, 5 g Prot, 85 mg Calc. *POINTS* value: *3.*

✹ FOOD NOTE Known as *sopa de lima* (lime soup), this classic soup hails from the Yucatán region of Mexico. Freshly squeezed lime juice and toasted corn tortilla strips lend this soup its authentic Mexican flavor. To make the soup more substantial, add 1 cup diced cooked chicken along with the broth and tomatoes (¼ cup chicken will increase the per-serving *POINTS* value by *1*).

Spiced-Up Pumpkin Soup

2 limes
2 teaspoons olive oil
1 large Spanish onion, chopped
2 teaspoons ground cumin
½ teaspoon cinnamon
⅛ teaspoon cayenne
5 cups canned vegetable broth
2 (15-ounce) cans solid-pack pumpkin
½ cup unsweetened applesauce
1 tablespoon sugar
¾ teaspoon salt
3 tablespoons fat-free half-and-half

HANDS-ON PREP 15 MIN
COOK 15 MIN
SERVES 6

1 Zest one of the limes, then squeeze enough juice from the limes to equal 2 tablespoons. Set the zest and juice aside.

2 Heat the oil in a Dutch oven over medium heat. Add the onion and cook, stirring frequently, until golden, about 6 minutes. Add the cumin, cinnamon, and cayenne; cook, stirring, until fragrant, about 30 seconds. Remove the mixture from the heat and let cool about 5 minutes.

3 Transfer the onion mixture to a food processor and add 1 cup of the broth; puree. Return the mixture to the Dutch oven; add the remaining 4 cups broth, the pumpkin, applesauce, sugar, and salt. Bring to a boil, stirring occasionally. Reduce the heat and simmer, covered, about 2 minutes. Stir in the reserved lime juice.

4 Ladle the soup into 6 bowls. Drizzle each with ½ tablespoon half-and-half and swirl lightly with the tip of a knife. Sprinkle with the reserved lime zest.

PER SERVING (1½ cups): 107 Cal, 2 g Fat, 1 g Sat Fat, 0 g Trans Fat, 0 mg Chol, 1148 mg Sod, 22 g Carb, 5 g Fib, 2 g Prot, 66 mg Calc. *POINTS* value: *2.*

☀ PLAY IT SAFE **Covering the soup pot while the soup simmers serves two purposes: It prevents the soup from bubbling onto the stove and also prevents it from getting too thick.**

Sweet and
Savory Salads

CHAPTER 3

**PERUVIAN CHICKEN-POTATO
SALAD**

Peruvian Chicken-Potato Salad

5 tablespoons fresh
lime juice

1 garlic clove, minced

1 tablespoon chili powder

½ teaspoon ground cumin

½ teaspoon salt

1 pound skinless boneless
chicken breast halves

2 pounds small purple or
red potatoes, halved

8 radishes, thinly sliced

5 scallions, thinly sliced

⅓ cup chopped fresh
cilantro

3 tablespoons olive oil

¼ teaspoon freshly ground
pepper

5 dashes hot pepper sauce,
or to taste

HANDS-ON PREP 15 MIN
COOK 15 MIN
SERVES 6

1 Combine 1 tablespoon of the lime juice, the garlic, chili powder, cumin, and salt in a small bowl. Rub the mixture on both sides of the chicken breasts. Put the coated breasts on a plate; cover and refrigerate at least 2 hours or up to 8 hours.

2 Place the potatoes in a large saucepan with enough water to cover by 2 inches and set over high heat; bring to a simmer. Cook until the potatoes are tender when pierced with a knife, about 15 minutes. Drain.

3 Meanwhile, spray the broiler rack with nonstick spray; preheat the broiler. Place the chicken on the broiler rack and broil 5 inches from the heat, turning once, until cooked through, about 10 minutes. Let stand at room temperature about 5 minutes. Slice the chicken on the diagonal into 1/2-inch-wide strips. Combine the chicken, potatoes, radishes, scallions, and cilantro in a serving bowl.

4 To make the dressing, whisk together the remaining 4 tablespoons lime juice, the oil, ground pepper, and pepper sauce in a small bowl. Drizzle over the salad and toss to coat. Serve at once or refrigerate, covered, up to 24 hours.

PER SERVING (1⅓ cups): 280 Cal, 10 g Fat, 2 g Sat Fat, 0 g Trans Fat, 46 mg Chol, 268 mg Sod, 30 g Carb, 5 g Fib, 20 g Prot, 59 mg Calc. *POINTS* value: *6.*

Colombian Beef and Onion Salad

1 (1-pound) flank steak, trimmed
1 large onion, sliced into ½-inch-thick rounds
2 celery stalks, thinly sliced
¼ cup chopped fresh cilantro
2 tablespoons balsamic vinegar
1 tablespoon olive oil
½ teaspoon instant espresso powder

HANDS-ON PREP 20 MIN
COOK 20 MIN
SERVES 4

1 Spray the grill rack with nonstick spray; prepare the grill. Place the steak and onion on the grill rack and grill until an instant-read thermometer inserted in the side of the steak registers 145°F for medium, about 5 minutes on each side. Transfer the steak to a cutting board and let stand about 5 minutes. Grill the onion, turning once, until softened, about 20 minutes. Transfer to a plate; set aside about 5 minutes.

2 Separate the onion into rings and put into a serving bowl. Add the celery and cilantro to the bowl. Thinly slice the steak on an angle against the grain; add to the bowl.

3 To make the dressing, whisk together the vinegar, oil, and espresso powder in a small bowl until the espresso powder is dissolved. Drizzle over the salad and gently toss to coat.

PER SERVING (1¼ cups): 231 Cal, 11 g Fat, 3 g Sat Fat, 0 g Trans Fat, 49 mg Chol, 53 mg Sod, 5 g Carb, 1 g Fib, 27 g Prot, 23 mg Calc. **POINTS** value: **5.**

✹ GOOD IDEA **If you happen to be a fan of red onions or any of the sweet onions (Vidalia, Texas Sweet, or Walla Walla) that are readily available in many supermarkets, feel free to use them instead. Just keep in mind that sweet onions won't contribute the same flavor punch to the salad as regular onions.**

Chicken Salad with Mango, Celery, and Lime

1 pound skinless boneless chicken breast halves

2 whole pimientos

2 garlic cloves

2 tablespoons fresh lime juice

½ teaspoon salt

¼ teaspoon freshly ground pepper

2 mangoes, pitted, peeled, and thinly sliced

6 scallions, thinly sliced

3 celery stalks, thinly sliced

HANDS-ON PREP 15 MIN
COOK 10 MIN
SERVES 4

1 Spray the broiler rack with nonstick spray; preheat the broiler. Place the chicken on the broiler rack and broil 5 inches from the heat, turning once, until cooked through, about 10 minutes. Transfer the chicken to a cutting board and let stand about 5 minutes. Slice on the diagonal into ½-inch-wide strips.

2 To make the dressing, put the pimientos, garlic, lime juice, salt, and pepper in a food processor or mini food processor and puree.

3 Combine the chicken, mangoes, scallions, and celery in a serving bowl. Pour the dressing over and gently toss to coat.

PER SERVING (1 cup): 230 Cal, 4 g Fat, 1 g Sat Fat, 0 g Trans Fat, 68 mg Chol, 393 mg Sod, 23 g Carb, 4 g Fib, 27 g Prot, 58 mg Calc. *POINTS* value: *4.*

GOOD IDEA **If you don't want to buy an entire bunch of celery for this recipe, shop the salad bar at your local market and buy about 1¼ cups sliced celery.**

Turkey, Black Bean, and Tomatillo Layered Salad

1 small onion, chopped
1 pound ground skinless
   turkey breast
1 tablespoon chili powder
1 teaspoon dried oregano
½ teaspoon salt
¼ teaspoon freshly ground
   pepper
4 cups shredded romaine
   lettuce
1 (15-ounce) can black
   beans, rinsed and
   drained
1 (12-ounce) can tomatillos,
   rinsed, drained, and
   chopped
½ cup plain fat-free yogurt
1 cup prepared fat-free
   salsa
Fresh cilantro sprigs, for
   garnish

HANDS-ON PREP 20 MIN
COOK 12 MIN
SERVES 4

1 Spray a large nonstick skillet with nonstick spray and set over medium heat. Add the onion and cook, stirring, until softened, about 5 minutes. Add the turkey and cook, breaking it up with a wooden spoon, until cooked through, about 5 minutes. Add the chili powder, oregano, salt, and pepper. Cook, stirring, until fragrant, about 20 seconds. Remove the skillet from the heat.

2 Layer the lettuce, beans, and tomatillos in a glass serving bowl. Top with the warm turkey mixture. Spoon the yogurt on top, then top with ½ cup of the salsa. Garnish with cilantrop sprigs and serve the remaining ½ cup salsa alongside.

PER SERVING (1¼ cups): 347 Cal, 8 g Fat, 2 g Sat Fat, 0 g Trans Fat, 76 mg Chol, 1051 mg Sod, 35 g Carb, 9 g Fib, 35 g Prot, 174 mg Calc. **POINTS** value: **7.**

✺ GOOD IDEA **If you happen to have some small glass salad bowls on hand, create individual layered salads another time. Layer the lettuce, beans, and tomatillos in the bowls, then cover and refrigerate up to 2 hours. Just before serving, cook up the turkey and proceed as directed.**

TURKEY, BLACK BEAN, AND
TOMATILLO LAYERED SALAD

GRAPEFRUIT AND SCALLOP SALAD

Grapefruit and Scallop Salad

1 pound sea scallops,
sliced into ¼-inch-thick
rounds
4 cups shredded romaine
lettuce
1 grapefruit, peeled and
sectioned
1 serrano chile pepper,
seeded and minced
(wear gloves to prevent
irritation)
¼ cup pecans, toasted
and chopped
1 small shallot, minced
2 tablespoons white-wine
vinegar
1 tablespoon fresh lime
juice
1 teaspoon Dijon mustard
½ teaspoon salt
¼ teaspoon freshly ground
pepper
¼ teaspoon crushed red
pepper
4 teaspoons olive oil

HANDS-ON PREP 25 MIN
COOK 15 MIN
SERVES 4

1 Bring a large saucepan of water to a gentle simmer.
Add the scallops and cook just until firm and opaque,
about 1½ minutes. Drain in a colander and cool briefly
under cold running water. Drain on paper towels.

2 Combine the scallops, lettuce, grapefruit, serrano
pepper, and pecans in a serving bowl.

3 To make the dressing, whisk together the shallot,
vinegar, lime juice, mustard, salt, ground pepper, and
crushed red pepper in a small bowl until blended;
slowly whisk in the oil. Drizzle the dressing over the
salad and gently toss to coat.

PER SERVING (1¼ cups): 188 Cal, 11 g Fat, 1 g Sat Fat,
0 g Trans Fat, 30 mg Chol, 483 mg Sod, 10 g Carb, 3 g Fib,
15 g Prot, 104 mg Calc. *POINTS* value: **4.**

✸ HOW WE DID IT **Toasting nuts brings out
their flavor and also crisps them. There are two easy
ways to toast nuts: Put them into a skillet over
medium heat and cook, tossing them occasionally,
until toasted, about 7 minutes. Or spread them on
the tray of a toaster oven and toast at 375°F, tossing
occasionally, until toasted, about 7 minutes. Be sure
to remove the toasted nuts from the skillet or tray at
once, or they will continue to cook and darken.**

Shrimp Salad with Orange and Red Onion

1 yellow bell pepper
1 small shallot, halved
2 tablespoons fresh lime juice
2 tablespoons fat-free sour cream
1 teaspoon ground cumin
½ teaspoon salt
¼ teaspoon freshly ground pepper
1 pound medium shrimp, peeled and deveined
2 cups shredded romaine lettuce
12 cherry tomatoes, halved
2 scallions, thinly sliced
1 orange, peeled and sectioned
1 small red onion, sliced into thin rounds
¼ cup chopped fresh cilantro

HANDS-ON PREP 25 MIN
COOK 17 MIN
SERVES 4

1 Preheat the broiler. Line a baking sheet with foil and place the pepper on it. Broil 5 inches from the heat, turning frequently with tongs, until the skin blisters, about 15 minutes. Wrap the pepper in the foil and let steam about 10 minutes.

2 Meanwhile, bring a large saucepan of water to a gentle simmer. When cool enough to handle, peel the bell pepper, remove the seeds, and cut into quarters.

3 To make the dressing, put the bell pepper, shallot, lime juice, sour cream, cumin, salt, and ground pepper in a food processor or a mini food processor and process until fairly smooth.

4 Add the shrimp to the simmering water and cook just until opaque in the center, about 2 minutes. Drain in a colander and cool under cold running water. Drain.

5 Combine the shrimp, lettuce, tomatoes, scallions, orange, onion, and cilantro in a serving bowl. Pour the dressing over and toss to coat.

PER SERVING (1 cup): 108 Cal, 1 g Fat, 0 g Sat Fat, 0 g Trans Fat, 107 mg Chol, 437 mg Sod, 13 g Carb, 3 g Fib, 13 g Prot, 73 mg Calc. **POINTS** value: *2.*

✹ EXPRESS LANE **If you don't want to go to the fuss of peeling and deveining the shrimp, have your fishmonger do it for you—or skip having to cook them altogether by buying cooked cocktail shrimp.**

Mexican Chopped Vegetable Salad

⅓ cup plain fat-free yogurt

2 tablespoons fresh lime juice

1 garlic clove, crushed through a press

1 teaspoon ground cumin

½ teaspoon cinnamon

½ teaspoon salt

1 (12-ounce) can tomatillos, rinsed, drained, and chopped

¼ pound fresh white or cremini mushrooms, chopped

1 large red bell pepper, seeded and chopped

1 large zucchini, chopped

1 small red onion, chopped

HANDS-ON PREP 20 MIN

COOK NONE

SERVES 6

1 To make the dressing, whisk together the yogurt, lime juice, garlic, cumin, cinnamon, and salt in a small bowl until blended.

2 Combine the tomatillos, mushrooms, bell pepper, zucchini, and onion in a serving bowl. Pour the dressing over and toss to coat.

PER SERVING (1 cup): 54 Cal, 1 g Fat, 0 g Sat Fat, 0 g Trans Fat, 0 mg Chol, 266 mg Sod, 10 g Carb, 3 g Fib, 3 g Prot, 51 mg Calc. *POINTS* value: *1.*

✸ HOW WE DID IT The secret to a great chopped salad is to chop each vegetable the same size. We think that half-inch pieces are just the right size for eating. You can make the salad ahead: Store the chopped vegetables and dressing in separate containers, tightly covered, in the refrigerator, up to 8 hours. Combine the vegetables and dressing just before serving.

Beefsteak Tomato, Cheese, and Herb Salad

2 large beefsteak
  tomatoes, each cut into
  6 thick slices
12 fresh basil leaves
12 fresh cilantro sprigs
½ cup crumbled queso
  blanco
2 tablespoons fresh lime
  juice
½ teaspoon kosher salt

HANDS-ON PREP 15 MIN
COOK NONE
SERVES 4

Place 3 tomato slices, 3 basil leaves, and 3 cilantro sprigs on each of 4 plates. Crumble 2 tablespoons cheese over each salad, then sprinkle each with ½ tablespoon lime juice and ⅛ teaspoon salt.

PER SERVING (1 tomato salad): 66 Cal, 4 g Fat, 2 g Sat Fat, 0 g Trans Fat, 14 mg Chol, 231 mg Sod, 5 g Carb, 1 g Fib, 4 g Prot, 74 mg Calc. **POINTS** value: **1.**

☼ TRY IT *Queso blanco* (KAY-soh BLAHN-koh) is a slightly salty fresh Mexican cheese with a texture similar to that of farmer cheese. It is sold in small containers in many supermarkets, specialty food stores, and Hispanic markets. It is also known as queso fresco (fresh cheese).

Costa Rican Slaw

½ cup fat-free mayonnaise
3 tablespoons fresh lime juice
1 teaspoon salt
¼ teaspoon freshly ground pepper
1 large green cabbage (about 2 pounds)
1 red bell pepper, seeded
1 large carrot
2 mangoes, pitted, peeled, and chopped
2 pickled jalapeño peppers, seeded and chopped
2 tablespoons chopped fresh cilantro

HANDS-ON PREP 20 MIN
COOK NONE
SERVES 8

1 To make the dressing, whisk together the mayonnaise, lime juice, salt, and ground pepper in a small bowl until blended.

2 Shred the cabbage, bell pepper, and carrot into a serving bowl using the large holes of a box grater. Add the mangoes, pickled jalapeños, and cilantro and gently toss to mix. Pour the dressing over and toss to coat.

PER SERVING (1 cup): 77 Cal, 1 g Fat, 0 g Sat Fat, 0 g Trans Fat, 2 mg Chol, 532 mg Sod, 18 g Carb, 4 g Fib, 2 g Prot, 56 mg Calc. *POINTS* value: *1.*

☀ EXPRESS LANE **If you're short on time, pick up a bag of shredded green cabbage in the produce section of the supermarket. It will cut way down on your prep time. You will need about 7 cups.**

Cucumber "Noodle" Salad

1 poblano chile pepper
1 shallot, quartered
3 tablespoons white-wine
   vinegar
½ teaspoon dry mustard
½ teaspoon salt
¼ teaspoon freshly ground
   pepper
2 large cucumbers, peeled
¼ cup chopped fresh
   cilantro

HANDS-ON PREP 20 MIN
COOK 10 MIN
SERVES 4

1 Char the poblano pepper by holding it with tongs over an open gas flame, turning often, until blackened on all sides, about 10 minutes. (Or preheat the broiler and broil the pepper 5 inches from the heat, turning often, until blackened all over, about 5 minutes.) Place the pepper in a paper bag or heavy zip-close plastic bag and seal the bag. Set aside about 10 minutes.

2 To make the dressing, when cool enough to handle, peel and seed the poblano pepper. Put the poblano, shallot, vinegar, dry mustard, salt, and ground pepper in a food processor or a mini food processor and puree.

3 To make the "noodles," hold 1 cucumber over a serving bowl and lightly pull a vegetable peeler down the length of the cucumber to shave off a long noodle. Make a few more noodles, then rotate the cucumber a quarter turn and peel more noodles. Peel noodles from all the sides of the cucumber until you get down to the seedy, pulpy center; discard the center. Repeat with the remaining cucumber.

4 Pour the dressing over the cucumber noodles. Add the cilantro and toss to coat. Serve at once or refrigerate, covered, up to 2 days.

PER SERVING (1 cup): 27 Cal, 0 g Fat, 0 g Sat Fat, 0 g Trans Fat, 0 mg Chol, 300 mg Sod, 5 g Carb, 1 g Fib, 1 g Prot, 28 mg Calc. **POINTS** value: **0.**

CUCUMBER "NOODLE" SALAD

Pinto Bean, Beet, and Bell Pepper Salad

1 (15-ounce) can pinto
   beans, rinsed and drained
1 (15-ounce) can beets,
   drained and chopped
2 celery stalks, chopped
1 red bell pepper, seeded
   and chopped
1 green bell pepper,
   seeded and chopped
1 small red onion, chopped
3 tablespoons fresh
   lemon juice
2 teaspoons ground cumin
1 teaspoon ground
   coriander
½ teaspoon salt
¼ teaspoon freshly ground
   pepper

HANDS-ON PREP 15 MIN
COOK NONE
SERVES 6

Combine the beans, beets, celery, bell peppers, and onion in a serving bowl. Add the lemon juice, cumin, coriander, salt, and ground pepper; toss to mix.

PER SERVING (1 cup): 105 Cal, 1 g Fat, 0 g Sat Fat, 0 g Trans Fat, 0 mg Chol, 391 mg Sod, 21 g Carb, 6 g Fib, 6 g Prot, 50 mg Calc. **POINTS** value: *1.*

✸ **EXPRESS LANE** Consider tossing together a double batch of this tasty salad; it can be refrigerated in an airtight container up to 2 days. Just be sure to toss it well before serving.

South-of-the-Border Fruit Salad

1 teaspoon cumin seeds

1 medium cantaloupe, peeled, seeded, and chopped

1 mango, pitted, peeled, and chopped

1 small grapefruit, peeled and sectioned

½ pint raspberries

1 small shallot, minced

1 tablespoon fresh lime juice

¼ teaspoon salt

HANDS-ON PREP 15 MIN
COOK 3 MIN
SERVES 6

1 Heat a small dry nonstick skillet over low heat. Add the cumin seeds and toast, shaking the pan often, until fragrant, about 3 minutes. Transfer the seeds to a small plate; cool about 5 minutes.

2 Combine the cantaloupe, mango, grapefruit, and raspberries in a serving bowl. Add the cumin seeds, shallot, lime juice, and salt; gently toss to coat.

PER SERVING (1¼ cups): 78 Cal, 1 g Fat, 0 g Sat Fat, 0 g Trans Fat, 0 mg Chol, 116 mg Sod, 19 g Carb, 3 g Fib, 2 g Prot, 27 mg Calc. *POINTS* value: *1.*

FOOD NOTE **Salt is the secret ingredient in fruit salads—it actually makes them taste sweeter. But be careful; a little goes a long way.**

Meat,
Latino-Style

CHAPTER 4

SEARED BEEF WITH
TOMATO-AVOCADO SALSA

Seared Beef with Tomato-Avocado Salsa

2 large plum tomatoes, seeded and chopped

¼ cup finely chopped red onion

¼ cup diced avocado

2 tablespoons fresh lime juice

1 tablespoon chopped fresh cilantro

¾ teaspoon salt

1 (¾-pound) beef tenderloin, trimmed

1½ teaspoons extra-virgin olive oil

1 poblano chile pepper, seeded and cut into thin strips (wear gloves to prevent irritation), optional

HANDS ON PREP 25 MIN
COOK 12 MIN
SERVES 4

1 To make the salsa, combine the tomatoes, onion, avocado, 1 tablespoon of the lime juice, the cilantro, and ¼ teaspoon of the salt in a serving bowl. Set aside.

2 Cut the beef lengthwise (with the grain) into 4 thick slices. Place each slice between 2 sheets of plastic wrap and pound with a meat mallet to ¼-inch thickness. Rub the beef with the remaining 1 tablespoon lime juice and ½ teaspoon salt.

3 Heat the oil in a large nonstick skillet set over medium-high heat. Add the beef and cook until browned and cooked through, about 4 minutes on each side. Transfer the beef to a plate and keep warm. Add the poblano pepper, if using, to the skillet and cook, stirring occasionally, until softened, 2–3 minutes. Place each piece of beef on a plate and top with one-fourth of the poblano pepper. Serve with the salsa.

PER SERVING (1 piece beef, ¼ of pepper, and about ⅓ cup salsa): 182 Cal, 9 g Fat, 3 g Sat Fat, 0 g Trans Fat, 37 mg Chol, 473 mg Sod, 4 g Carb, 2 g Fib, 20 g Prot, 14 mg Calc. *POINTS* value: *4.*

✺ FOOD NOTE **Seared beef (*carne asada*) is one of the most popular and simplest of beef preparations in Mexico. Invented in the 1940s by restaurateur José Loredo, the dish always features steak that has been sprinkled with lime juice and salt, then quickly seared.**

Filet Mignon with Ancho Chile Sauce

2 dried ancho chile peppers, seeded (wear gloves to prevent irritation)
3 cups boiling water
2 garlic cloves, unpeeled
1 cup reduced-sodium beef broth
¼ teaspoon dried oregano
⅛ teaspoon ground cumin
1 teaspoon olive oil
¼ cup unsweetened applesauce
¾ teaspoon salt
4 (3-ounce) filet mignons, ½ inch thick, trimmed
¼ teaspoon freshly ground pepper

HANDS-ON PREP 10 MIN
COOK 45 MIN
SERVES 4

1 Heat a medium nonstick skillet over medium heat. Add the ancho chiles; toast until fragrant, about 30 seconds on each side. Transfer to a bowl; cover with the boiling water. Let stand 20 minutes. Drain; discard the water.

2 Set the same skillet over medium heat. Add the garlic and cook, shaking the pan occasionally, until browned in spots, about 8 minutes. Transfer the garlic to a plate. When cool enough to handle, peel the garlic. Put the chiles, garlic, ½ cup of the broth, the oregano, and cumin in a blender; process until smooth, 1–2 minutes.

3 Heat the oil in the same skillet over medium-high heat. Add the chile mixture and cook, stirring occasionally, until very thick, 3–5 minutes. Add the remaining ½ cup broth, the applesauce, and ¼ teaspoon of the salt; bring to a boil. Reduce the heat and simmer, stirring occasionally, until thickened, 15–18 minutes.

4 Meanwhile, spray the broiler rack with nonstick spray; preheat the broiler. Sprinkle the filets with the remaining salt and the ground pepper. Place on the broiler rack. Broil 4 inches from the heat until an instant-read thermometer registers 145°F for medium, 3–4 minutes on each side. Transfer the steaks to 4 plates and top with the ancho pepper sauce.

PER SERVING (1 filet and 3 tablespoons sauce): 172 Cal, 7 g Fat, 2 g Sat Fat, 0 g Trans Fat, 37 mg Chol, 514 mg Sod, 5 g Carb, 1 g Fib, 21 g Prot, 16 mg Calc. **POINTS** value: **4.**

Honey-Chipotle Marinated T-bone Steaks

1 canned chipotle chile en adobo, minced
2 tablespoons honey
1 garlic clove, minced
½ teaspoon chili powder
½ teaspoon ground coriander
½ teaspoon ground cumin
¼ teaspoon ground fennel (optional)
2 (1½- to 1¾-pound) T-bone steaks, about ½ inch thick, trimmed
½ teaspoon salt

HANDS-ON PREP 10 MIN
COOK 10 MIN
SERVES 6

1 To make the rub, combine the chipotle en adobo, honey, garlic, chili powder, coriander, cumin, and fennel in a small bowl. Rub the mixture on both sides of the steaks. Place the steaks on a plate; cover and refrigerate at least 1 hour or up to 24 hours.

2 Spray the broiler rack with nonstick spray and preheat the broiler.

3 Place the steaks on the broiler rack and broil 4 inches from the heat until an instant-read thermometer inserted in the side of the steak registers 145°F for medium, about 5 minutes on each side. Cut each steak into 3 portions, making a total of 6 pieces.

PER SERVING (1 piece steak): 244 Cal, 9 g Fat, 4 g Sat Fat, 0 g Trans Fat, 59 mg Chol, 328 mg Sod, 7 g Carb, 0 g Fib, 32 g Prot, 14 mg Calc. **POINTS** value: **6.**

✸ TRY IT **T-bone steak is basically the same cut as a porterhouse, except it has a smaller piece of the tenderloin (filet) attached. The honey in the marinade helps to counterbalance the spiciness of the chipotle chile. For a less spicy version, use half a chipotle chile, or leave it out altogether and substitute 1 teaspoon of smoked paprika, which is sweet paprika with an enticingly smoky essence.**

Spinach, Bell Pepper, and Flank Steak Roll

1 (1½-pound) flank steak, trimmed
2 tablespoons red-wine vinegar
2 garlic cloves, minced
1 teaspoon dried oregano
¾ teaspoon salt
⅛ teaspoon cayenne
2 tablespoons grated Parmesan cheese
1 cup packed fresh spinach leaves
1 red bell pepper, seeded and cut into thin strips
1 carrot, halved crosswise and cut into thin strips
1 (14½-ounce) can reduced-sodium beef broth

HANDS-ON PREP 20 MIN
COOK 1 HR 35 MIN
SERVES 6

1 Place the steak between 2 sheets of plastic wrap and pound to ¼-inch thickness with a meat mallet. Combine the vinegar, garlic, and oregano in a small bowl. Rub on both sides of the steak; refrigerate at least 2 hours.

2 Place the steak on a work surface with a long side facing you; sprinkle with the salt, cayenne, and Parmesan. Arrange the spinach on top of the cheese. Place the bell pepper and carrot lengthwise along the center. Roll the steak up lengthwise, jelly-roll style, then secure with kitchen string at 1-inch intervals.

3 Place the roll in a Dutch oven; add the broth and enough water come two-thirds of the way up the sides of the steak; bring to a boil. Reduce the heat and simmer, covered, turning occasionally, until the steak is very tender, about 1½ hours.

4 Transfer the meat to a cutting board and let stand about 10 minutes. Cut into 12 slices and serve topped with some of the braising liquid.

PER SERVING (2 slices steak and ¼ cup braising liquid): 214 Cal, 9 g Fat, 3 g Sat Fat, 0 g Trans Fat, 51 mg Chol, 429 mg Sod, 4 g Carb, 1 g Fib, 29 g Prot, 51 mg Calc. *POINTS* value: *5.*

☀ GOOD IDEA **This dish can be served hot or cold. If serving cold, allow the meat to cool in the braising liquid for 25–30 minutes, then drain and wrap tightly in plastic wrap. Refrigerate up to 2 days. Slice and arrange on a platter just before serving.**

SPINACH, BELL PEPPER, AND
FLANK STEAK ROLL

Mustard-Lime Grilled Sirloin

¼ cup fresh lime juice

2 garlic cloves, minced

1 jalapeño chile pepper, seeded and finely chopped (wear gloves to prevent irritation)

2 tablespoons chopped fresh cilantro

1 tablespoon Dijon mustard

1 teaspoon ground cumin

1 (1-pound) boneless sirloin steak, trimmed

¾ teaspoon salt

¼ teaspoon freshly ground pepper

1 onion, cut into 4 thick rounds

HANDS-ON PREP 15 MIN
COOK 10 MIN
SERVES 4

1 To make the marinade, combine the lime juice, garlic, jalapeño pepper, cilantro, mustard, and cumin in a shallow baking dish. Add the steak and turn to coat. Cover and refrigerate, turning the steak occasionally, about 2 hours.

2 Spray the grill rack with olive oil nonstick spray; prepare the grill.

3 Sprinkle the steak with ½ teaspoon of the salt and ⅛ teaspoon of the ground pepper. Sprinkle the onion with the remaining ¼ teaspoon salt and ⅛ teaspoon ground pepper. Place the steak and onion on the grill rack. Grill, covered, until an instant-read thermometer inserted in the side of the steak registers 145°F for medium, 8–10 minutes, and the onion is tender, about 10 minutes. Transfer the steak to a cutting board and loosely cover with foil; let stand about 5 minutes. Cut the steak across the grain into 12 slices and serve with the onion.

PER SERVING (3 slices meat and 1 slice onion): 157 Cal, 4 g Fat, 1 g Sat Fat, 0 g Trans Fat, 64 mg Chol, 500 mg Sod, 3 g Carb, 1 g Fib, 26 g Prot, 13 mg Calc. *POINTS* value: **3.**

☀ HOW WE DID IT **It is important not to overmarinate the steak in this recipe. If left too long in the marinade, the lime juice will cause the steak to take on an unpleasant mealy texture.**

Ropa Vieja

1 (1-pound) flank steak, trimmed
1 (14½-ounce) can reduced-sodium beef broth
5 garlic cloves, peeled
1 teaspoon extra-virgin olive oil
1 onion, chopped
2 tomatoes, coarsely chopped
1 celery stalk, chopped
1 carrot, chopped
1 jalapeño chile pepper, seeded and finely chopped (wear gloves to prevent irritation)
1 teaspoon dried oregano
¼ teaspoon salt
2 tablespoons chopped fresh cilantro

HANDS-ON PREP 20 MIN
COOK 1 HR 10 MIN
SERVES 4

1 Combine the flank steak, broth, and 3 of the garlic cloves in a medium nonstick skillet; bring to a boil. Reduce the heat and simmer, covered, until the steak is very tender, about 1 hour. Remove from the heat and let the steak rest in the broth about 15 minutes. Reserve ½ cup of the broth and discard the remaining broth, or refrigerate, covered, for another use. Transfer the steak to a cutting board; with 2 forks, shred the beef. Set aside.

2 Mince the remaining 2 garlic cloves. Wipe the skillet clean. Heat the oil in the skillet over medium-high heat. Add the onion and garlic; cook, stirring occasionally, until slightly softened, about 3 minutes. Add the tomatoes, celery, carrot, jalapeño pepper, oregano, and salt; cook, stirring occasionally, until softened, 3–4 minutes. Stir in the shredded beef and the reserved ½ cup broth. Cook, stirring occasionally, until most of the liquid is evaporated, 3–4 minutes. Remove from the heat and stir in the cilantro.

PER SERVING (¾ cup): 244 Cal, 10 g Fat, 3 g Sat Fat, 0 g Trans Fat, 49 mg Chol, 281 mg Sod, 10 g Carb, 2 g Fib, 29 g Prot, 43 mg Calc. *POINTS* value: **5.**

☼ TRY IT *Ropa vieja* (ROH-pah vee-EH-ha) means "old clothes" in Spanish and refers to the shredded appearance of the cooked beef. This very flavorful dish can be eaten with brown rice and vegetables or used as a filling for tacos, enchiladas, or burritos.

SPICY YUCATÁN BEEF TACOS

Spicy Yucatán Beef Tacos

2 plum tomatoes, cut into
  ¼-inch dice
½ small onion, finely
  chopped
1 tablespoon fresh lime
  juice
½ chipotle en adobo,
  minced or ½ teaspoon
  chipotle chile powder
1 tablespoon chopped
  fresh cilantro
½ teaspoon salt
2 teaspoons olive oil
1 (¾-pound) beef
  tenderloin, trimmed and
  cut into thin strips
1 onion, thinly sliced
¾ teaspoon Mexican, chili,
  or taco seasoning
4 (6-inch) corn tortillas
Torn leaf lettuce leaves
  (optional)

HANDS-ON PREP 15 MIN
COOK 12 MIN
SERVES 4

1 To make the salsa, combine the tomatoes, chopped onion, lime juice, chipotle en adobo, cilantro, and ¼ teaspoon of the salt in a medium bowl; set aside.

2 Heat the oil in a large nonstick skillet over medium-high heat. Add the beef and cook, stirring occasionally, until no longer pink, about 3 minutes. Transfer the beef to a plate.

3 Add the sliced onion to the same skillet. Cook, stirring occasionally, until the onion begins to brown, about 4 minutes. Return the beef to the skillet; add the Mexican seasoning and the remaining ¼ teaspoon salt. Cook, stirring occasionally, until the beef is cooked through, about 2 minutes.

4 Meanwhile, warm the tortillas according to the package directions. Top each tortilla with about ½ cup of the beef mixture, ¼ cup of the salsa, and some lettuce, if using.

PER SERVING (1 taco): 234 Cal, 9 g Fat, 3 g Sat Fat, 0 g Trans Fat, 37 mg Chol, 457 mg Sod, 17 g Carb, 3 g Fib, 22 g Prot, 61 mg Calc. *POINTS* value: *5.*

☀ GOOD IDEA **An authentic alternative to the salsa would be thinly sliced onion that has been sprinkled with fresh lime juice and salt, then topped with fresh cilantro leaves and thin slices of jalapeño pepper.**

Cuban Beef and Butternut Squash Stew

2 teaspoons olive oil

1 onion, chopped

3 garlic cloves, minced

1½ pounds beef eye round, trimmed and cut into 1-inch chunks

1 (14½-ounce) can reduced-sodium beef broth

2 tomatoes, chopped

½ teaspoon salt

¼ teaspoon freshly ground pepper

1 pound butternut squash, peeled, seeded, and cut into 1½-inch chunks

1 large sweet potato (about 1 pound), peeled and cut into 1½-inch chunks

2 corn-on-the-cob, husks and silk removed and each cut into 6 pieces

1 large zucchini, cut into 1-inch chunks

1 tablespoon fresh lime juice

HANDS-ON PREP 20 MIN
COOK 1 HR 40 MIN
SERVES 6

1 Heat the oil in a large nonstick Dutch oven over medium-high heat. Add the onion and garlic; cook, stirring occasionally, until beginning to soften, about 3 minutes. Add the beef and cook, turning occasionally, until beginning to brown, 4–5 minutes. Stir in the broth, tomatoes, salt, and pepper; bring to a boil. Reduce the heat and simmer, covered, about 1 hour.

2 Add the squash, sweet potato, corn, and zucchini to the Dutch oven; bring to a boil. Reduce the heat and simmer, covered, stirring occasionally, until the beef and vegetables are tender, about 30 minutes. Remove from the heat and stir in the lime juice.

PER SERVING (2 cups): 302 Cal, 6 g Fat, 2 g Sat Fat, 0 g Trans Fat, 64 mg Chol, 315 mg Sod, 33 g Carb, 5 g Fib, 31 g Prot, 69 mg Calc. *POINTS* value: *6.*

✺ HOW WE DID IT In this recipe, neither cornstarch nor flour is used to thicken the stew. As the sweet potato and squash cook, some of the pieces break down and gently thicken the broth just the right amount.

Spanish Meatballs in Sauce

1 onion, finely chopped

2 garlic cloves, minced

1 plum tomato, seeded and chopped

1 pound ground lean beef (7% or less fat)

½ cup dried seasoned bread crumbs

1 egg white

2 tablespoons grated Romano cheese

¼ teaspoon salt

¼ teaspoon freshly ground pepper

1 teaspoon dried oregano

1 cup reduced-sodium beef broth

1 cup dry red wine

HANDS ON PREP 15 MIN
COOK 33 MIN
SERVES 4

1 Spray a large nonstick skillet with nonstick spray and set over medium-high heat. Add half of the onion and all the garlic; cook, stirring occasionally, until beginning to soften, about 3 minutes. Stir in the tomato and cook until the juices evaporate, about 3 minutes. Transfer to a large bowl and let cool about 5 minutes.

2 Add the beef, bread crumbs, egg white, cheese, salt, and ⅛ teaspoon of the pepper to the onion mixture; mix well. Shape the mixture into 20 meatballs.

3 Wipe the skillet clean. Spray the skillet with nonstick spray and set over medium-high heat. Add the meatballs and cook, turning often, until browned, about 6 minutes. Transfer to a plate; set aside.

4 Wipe the skillet clean. Spray with nonstick spray and set over medium-high heat. Add the remaining onion and the oregano; cook, stirring occasionally, until softened, about 4 minutes. Add the broth, wine, and the remaining ⅛ teaspoon pepper; bring to a boil. Reduce the heat and simmer about 5 minutes. Return the meatballs to the skillet and gently simmer, covered, turning occasionally, until the meatballs are cooked through and the sauce is slightly reduced, about 15 minutes. Divide the meatballs among 4 bowls and top with the sauce.

PER SERVING (5 meatballs and ⅓ cup sauce): 270 Cal, 9 g Fat, 4 g Sat Fat, 0 g Trans Fat, 68 mg Chol, 400 mg Sod, 17 g Carb, 2 g Fib, 28 g Prot, 99 mg Calc. *POINTS* value: *6.*

Picadillo with Tortilla Crisps

6 (6-inch) corn tortillas,
each cut into 8 wedges
⅓ cup raisins
1 cup boiling water
1 pound ground lean beef
(7% or less fat)
1 onion, chopped
3 garlic cloves, minced
1 jalapeño chile pepper,
seeded and finely
chopped (wear gloves to
prevent irritation)
10 small pimiento-stuffed
green olives, halved
1 large tomato, chopped
2 tablespoons tomato
paste
1 teaspoon dried oregano
¾ teaspoon salt
1 (8-ounce) can pineapple
chunks in juice, drained

HANDS-ON PREP 15 MIN
COOK 25 MIN
SERVES 6

1 Preheat the oven to 425°F. Lightly spray a large
baking sheet with nonstick spray.

2 Arrange the tortilla wedges in a single layer on the
baking sheet and lightly spray with nonstick spray. Bake
until crisp, 6–8 minutes. Transfer the tortillas to a rack.

3 Meanwhile, place the raisins in a bowl and cover
with the boiling water. Let stand about 10 minutes;
drain and reserve.

4 Heat a large nonstick skillet over medium-high heat.
Add the beef and cook, breaking it up with a wooden
spoon, until beginning to brown, 4–5 minutes. Add the
onion, garlic, jalapeño pepper, and olives; cook, stirring
occasionally, until softened, 5–6 minutes. Stir in the
tomato, tomato paste, oregano, and salt; cook until the
tomato softens, 4–5 minutes. Stir in the reserved
raisins and the pineapple; cook until heated through,
2–3 minutes. Spoon the mixture onto plates and serve
with the tortilla crisps.

PER SERVING (⅔ cup picadillo and 8 tortilla crisps): 232 Cal,
7 g Fat, 2 g Sat Fat, 0 g Trans Fat, 43 mg Chol, 501 mg Sod,
27 g Carb, 3 g Fib, 17 g Prot, 74 mg Calc. **POINTS** value: **5.**

☼ ZAP IT Got leftovers? Our tasty picadillo can
be quickly reheated in the microwave: Place ⅔ cup
picadillo in a microwavable bowl and microwave on
High until hot, about 1½ minutes.

DRIED CHILE PEPPERS

Consider the taste difference between a grape and a raisin and you will understand why dried chiles add so much complexity of flavor and variety to dishes. Here's a glossary of some commonly used dried chiles that make Latin American food so special:

ANCHO This is the dried form of the poblano chile pepper. With an almost meaty flavor, it can be stuffed, chopped, or used in sauces.

CAYENNE Measuring 2 to 4 inches in length and about ½ inch across, this bright red pepper has a pungent heat, with a flavor that is both smoky and tart. It is mostly used ground.

CHIPOTLE Dark brown and leathery, this is the dried, smoked version of a jalapeño . It is not usually necessary to remove the stem and seeds, as it is added whole to many dishes. The canned version, chipotle en adobo sauce, is packed in a richly flavored sauce.

CHILE DE ARBOL This very, very hot pepper is about 3 inches long, slender, and reddish in color. It is most often used ground with other spices and added to soups and stews.

PASILLA About 6 inches long, this blackish pepper is mild and fragrant. It is used frequently in sauces and as a condiment.

Pork with Red Mole Sauce

3 dried pasilla chile
  peppers, seeded (wear
  gloves to prevent
  irritation)
3 cups boiling water
1 cup reduced-sodium
  chicken broth
6 (¼-pound) boneless
  center-cut pork loin
  chops, ¾ inch thick,
  trimmed
1 teaspoon salt
¼ teaspoon freshly ground
  pepper
3 teaspoons olive oil
3 garlic cloves, peeled
1 onion, chopped
1 tomato, quartered
½ teaspoon dried oregano
½ teaspoon ground cumin
¼ teaspoon cinnamon
1 ounce semisweet
  chocolate, chopped
3 cups hot cooked
  white rice

HANDS-ON PREP 20 MIN
COOK 24 MIN
SERVES 6

1 Heat a nonstick skillet over medium-high heat. Add the chiles and toast about 30 seconds on each side. Transfer to a bowl; cover with the boiling water; let stand until hydrated, about 20 minutes. Drain. Transfer the chiles to a blender. Add ½ cup of the broth; process until smooth, 1–2 minutes. Return to the same bowl.

2 Sprinkle the pork with ½ teaspoon of the salt and the ground pepper. Heat 1 teaspoon of the oil in the same skillet over medium-high heat. Add the pork chops and cook until browned, about 1½ minutes on each side. Transfer the pork to a plate and set aside. Add 1 teaspoon oil, the garlic, and onion to the skillet; cook until golden, 2–3 minutes. Stir in the tomato and cook until softened, about 2 minutes. Add the oregano, cumin, and cinnamon; cook until fragrant, about 15 seconds.

3 Spoon the tomato mixture into the blender. Add the remaining broth; process until smooth, about 2 minutes.

4 Heat the remaining 1 teaspoon oil in the same skillet over medium heat. Add the pepper mixture, tomato mixture, and the remaining ½ teaspoon salt; cook, stirring, until thickened, about 6 minutes. Stir in the chocolate and cook, stirring, until melted. Add the pork and turn to coat with the sauce. Simmer until cooked through, 6–8 minutes. Serve with the rice.

PER SERVING (1 pork chop, ¼ cup sauce, and ½ cup rice): 358 Cal, 13 g Fat, 4 g Sat Fat, 0 g Trans Fat, 72 mg Chol, 833 mg Sod, 30 g Carb, 2 g Fib, 29 g Prot, 35 mg Calc. *POINTS* value: *8.*

Chile-Marinated Pork Tenderloin

3 dried ancho chile
   peppers, seeded (wear
   gloves to prevent
   irritation)
3 cups boiling water
3 garlic cloves, peeled
2 tablespoons cold water
2 tablespoons ketchup
2 teaspoons extra-virgin
   olive oil
1 teaspoon dried oregano
1 teaspoon ground cumin
½ teaspoon ground allspice
1 (1-pound) pork
   tenderloin, trimmed
¾ teaspoon salt

HANDS-ON PREP 12 MIN
COOK 35 MIN
SERVES 4

1 Set a medium nonstick skillet over medium-heat. Add the ancho chiles and toast just until very fragrant, about 30 seconds on each side. Transfer to a medium bowl and cover with the boiling water; let stand until hydrated, about 20 minutes. Drain the peppers and discard the water. Transfer the chiles to a blender. Add the garlic, cold water, ketchup, oil, oregano, cumin, and allspice; process until smooth, 1–2 minutes.

2 Place the pork in a zip-close plastic bag and add the pepper mixture. Squeeze out the air and seal the bag; turn to coat the pork. Refrigerate, turning the bag occasionally, at least 4 hours or up to 10 hours.

3 Preheat the oven to 450°F. Place a rack in a shallow roasting pan and spray with nonstick spray. Remove the pork from the marinade and discard the marinade. Wipe off the pork with paper towels. Sprinkle the pork with the salt and place on the rack.

4 Roast until an instant-read thermometer inserted in the center of the pork registers 160°F for medium, 30–35 minutes. Transfer to a cutting board and cover loosely with foil; let stand about 10 minutes. Cut into 12 slices and serve hot or at room temperature.

PER SERVING (3 slices pork): 160 Cal, 5 g Fat, 2 g Sat Fat, 0 g Trans Fat, 72 mg Chol, 515 mg Sod, 1 g Carb, 0 g Fib, 26 g Prot, 11 mg Calc. **POINTS** value: *4.*

Cuban-Style Christmas Eve Pork Roast

5 garlic cloves, minced
3 tablespoons fresh lime juice
3 tablespoons fresh lemon juice
1 tablespoon olive oil
1 teaspoon dried oregano
1 (2-pound) boneless pork loin, trimmed
1 teaspoon salt
¼ teaspoon freshly ground pepper

HANDS-ON PREP 10 MIN
COOK 45 MIN
SERVES 8

1 To make the marinade, combine the garlic, lime juice, lemon juice, oil, and oregano in a zip-close plastic bag; add the pork. Squeeze out the air and seal the bag; turn the bag to coat the pork. Refrigerate, turning the bag occasionally, about 3 hours.

2 Meanwhile, preheat the oven to 425°F. Place a rack in a shallow roasting pan and spray with nonstick spray. Remove the pork from the plastic bag and discard the marinade. Place the pork on the rack and sprinkle with the salt and pepper.

3 Roast until an instant-read thermometer inserted in the center of the pork registers 160°F for medium, 40–45 minutes. Transfer to a cutting board and cover loosely with foil; let stand about 10 minutes. Cut the pork into 16 slices and arrange on a platter.

PER SERVING (2 slices pork): 192 Cal, 9 g Fat, 3 g Sat Fat, 0 g Trans Fat, 72 mg Chol, 339 mg Sod, 0 g Carb, 0 g Fib, 25 g Prot, 7 mg Calc. **POINTS** value: **5.**

✹ GOOD IDEA Use any leftovers of this special pork roast, *lechón asado* in Spanish, to make a Cuban pressed sandwich: Fill 2 slices of light Italian bread that have been brushed with Dijon mustard with 1 very thin slice each of the pork, turkey breast, ham, reduced-fat Swiss cheese, and 2 slices of pickle. Grill the sandwich in a hot skillet (weighted with another skillet) until the cheese melts.

CUBAN-STYLE
CHRISTMAS EVE PORK
ROAST WITH RED BEANS
AND RICE, PAGE 171

PORK CHOPS WITH PRUNES
AND RED PEPPER

Pork Chops with Prunes and Red Pepper

3 teaspoons olive oil

1 onion, thinly sliced

2 garlic cloves, minced

1 red bell pepper, seeded and thinly sliced

10 pitted prunes, quartered

1 tomato, chopped

¾ cup reduced-sodium chicken broth

¾ teaspoon salt

¼ teaspoon freshly ground pepper

1 tablespoon chopped fresh cilantro

4 (¼-pound) boneless center-cut pork loin chops, ¾ inch thick, trimmed

2 cups hot cooked white rice

HANDS-ON PREP 15 MIN
COOK 20 MIN
SERVES 4

1 Heat 2 teaspoons of the oil in a medium nonstick skillet over medium-high heat. Add the onion and garlic; cook, stirring occasionally, until beginning to soften, about 3 minutes. Stir in the bell pepper and cook until softened, about 3 minutes. Add the prunes and tomato; cook until the tomato softens, about 2 minutes.

2 Add the broth, ¼ teaspoon of the salt, and ⅛ teaspoon of the pepper to the same skillet; bring to a boil. Cook until the mixture thickens, about 4 minutes. Remove the skillet from the heat and stir in the cilantro. Transfer to a bowl and keep warm.

3 Sprinkle the pork chops with the remaining ½ teaspoon salt and ⅛ teaspoon pepper. Wipe the skillet clean. Add the remaining 1 teaspoon oil to the skillet and heat over medium-high heat. Add the pork chops and cook until browned and cooked through, 4–5 minutes on each side. Place 1 pork chop on each of 4 plates and top with some of the warm prune mixture. Serve with the rice.

PER SERVING (1 pork chop, about ⅓ cup fruit mixture, and ½ cup rice): 398 Cal, 13 g Fat, 4 g Sat Fat, 0 g Trans Fat, 72 mg Chol, 895 mg Sod, 42 g Carb, 3 g Fib, 29 g Prot, 41 mg Calc. *POINTS* value: **8.**

✹ MAKE IT CORE **Omit the prunes, add an extra chopped tomato, and serve with cooked brown rice instead of the white.**

Apple Jelly and Chipotle–Glazed Pork Chops

¼ cup apple jelly
1 teaspoon grated lime zest
¼ teaspoon chipotle chile powder
4 (¼-pound) boneless center-cut pork loin chops, trimmed
1 teaspoon olive oil
1½ teaspoons Mexican, chili, or taco seasoning
½ teaspoon salt

HANDS-ON PREP 8 MIN
COOK 8 MIN
SERVES 4

1 Spray a broiler rack with nonstick spray and preheat the broiler.

2 Combine the jelly, lime zest, and chipotle chile powder in a small bowl. Set aside.

3 Rub the pork chops with the oil and sprinkle with the Mexican seasoning and salt. Place the pork chops on the broiler rack. Broil 5 inches from the heat, until beginning to brown, about 4 minutes. Brush the pork with half of the jelly mixture. Turn the pork and broil 2 minutes. Brush with the remaining jelly mixture and broil until cooked through, about 2 minutes longer.

PER SERVING (1 pork chop): 252 Cal, 10 g Fat, 3 g Sat Fat, 0 g Trans Fat, 72 mg Chol, 404 mg Sod, 14 g Carb, 0 g Fib, 25 g Prot, 14 mg Calc. **POINTS** value: **6.**

☀ TRY IT Chipotle chile powder, sometimes called ground chipotle pepper, is available in large supermarkets and in Hispanic markets. It can add a delectable heat to almost any rub or marinade. Just remember that a little bit goes a long way

Plantain, Raisin, and Pork Stew with Ancho Chiles

¼ cup packed golden
  raisins
3½ cups boiling water
3 dried ancho chile
  peppers, seeded
  (wear gloves to prevent
  irritation)
3 teaspoons canola oil
1 very ripe plantain, cut
  into ¼-inch-thick slices
1 large plum tomato,
  chopped
2 garlic cloves, thinly sliced
2 tablespoons salted
  peanuts
1 teaspoon ground cumin
¼ teaspoon cinnamon
¼ cup cold water
1 pound pork tenderloin,
  trimmed and cut into
  1-inch chunks
¾ teaspoon salt

HANDS-ON PREP 15 MIN
COOK 20 MIN
SERVES 4

1 Place the raisins in a small bowl and add ½ cup of the boiling water. Set aside until hydrated, about 10 minutes.

2 Meanwhile, heat a large nonstick skillet over medium-heat. Add the ancho chiles and toast, about 30 seconds on each side. Transfer to a medium bowl and cover with the remaining 3 cups boiling water. Let stand until hydrated, about 20 minutes; drain.

3 Heat 2 teaspoons of the oil in the same skillet over medium-high heat. Add the plantain, tomato, garlic, and peanuts; cook, stirring occasionally, until the plantain softens, 4–5 minutes. Add the cumin and cinnamon; cook until fragrant, about 30 seconds. Remove the skillet from the heat.

4 Put the raisins and soaking liquid, chiles, plantain mixture, and cold water in a blender; process until smooth. Sprinkle the pork with ½ teaspoon of the salt. Wipe the skillet clean and heat the remaining 1 teaspoon oil in the skillet. Add the pork and cook, stirring occasionally, until browned, about 4 minutes. Add the plantain mixture and the remaining ¼ teaspoon salt. Reduce the heat and simmer, stirring often, until the pork is cooked through, 4–5 minutes. Thin the sauce with water, if needed.

PER SERVING (generous ½ cup) 321 Cal, 11 g Fat, 2 g Sat Fat, 0 g Trans Fat, 72 mg Chol, 515 mg Sod, 30 g Carb, 3 g Fib, 28 g Prot, 31 mg Calc. **POINTS** value: **7**

Shredded Pork and Onion Tacos

1 (1-pound) pork
   tenderloin, trimmed and
   cut into 4 pieces
1 (14½-ounce) can
   reduced-sodium chicken
   broth
2 onions, sliced
3 garlic cloves, peeled
1 teaspoon ground cumin
2 teaspoons olive oil
½ teaspoon salt
4 (6-inch) whole-wheat
   flour tortillas
2 jalapeño chile peppers,
   each sliced into 8 rings
   (wear gloves to prevent
   irritation)
¼ cup packed fresh cilantro
   leaves
1 lime, cut into 4 wedges

HANDS-ON PREP 20 MIN
COOK 55 MIN
SERVES 4

1 Combine the pork, broth, half of the onions, the garlic, and cumin in a large skillet; bring to a boil. Reduce the heat and simmer, covered, until the meat is very tender, about 40 minutes. Remove the skillet from the heat. Let the pork cool, uncovered, in the broth about 15 minutes. Reserve ½ cup of the broth; discard the remaining broth. Transfer the pork to a cutting board and, using 2 forks, shred it.

2 Heat the oil in a medium nonstick skillet over medium-high heat. Add the shredded pork and sprinkle with the salt. Cook, stirring often, until lightly crisped, 4–5 minutes. Stir in the reserved broth and cook until the liquid is reduced by half, about 30 seconds.

3 Warm the tortillas according to the package directions. Top each with about ½ cup of the shredded pork, ¼ of the remaining onions, 4 jalapeño rings, and 1 tablespoon cilantro. Squeeze the juice of 1 lime wedge over each taco and serve at once.

PER SERVING (1 taco): 252 Cal, 7 g Fat, 2 g Sat Fat, 0 g Trans Fat, 72 mg Chol, 568 mg Sod, 17 g Carb, 3 g Fib, 29 g Prot, 36 mg Calc. **POINTS** value: **5.**

☀ HOW WE DID IT We have a special reason for crisping the pork in step 2. We just love the contrast of the crispy pork and the soft, warm tortillas. For an even more delicious contrast, top the tacos with some chopped tomato and crisp shredded lettuce for no additional **POINTS** value.

Pork Skewers with Lemon and Saffron

½ small onion, thinly sliced

2 garlic cloves, minced

2 tablespoons chopped
   fresh parsley

1 tablespoon chopped
   fresh cilantro

1 tablespoon fresh lemon
   juice

2 teaspoons olive oil

1 teaspoon paprika

½ teaspoon ground
   coriander

¼ teaspoon saffron threads,
   crushed

1 pound pork tenderloin,
   trimmed and cut into
   1-inch chunks

½ teaspoon salt

HANDS-ON PREP 15 MIN
COOK 8 MIN
SERVES 4

1 To make the marinade, combine the onion, garlic, parsley, cilantro, lemon juice, oil, paprika, coriander, and saffron in a zip-close plastic bag; add the pork. Squeeze out the air and seal the bag; turn to coat the pork. Refrigerate, turning the bag occasionally, at least 8 hours or up to 24 hours.

2 Spray the broiler rack with olive oil nonstick spray and preheat the broiler.

3 Thread 5 pieces of pork onto each of 4 metal skewers (if using wooden skewers, soak in warm water about 30 minutes); sprinkle with the salt. Place the skewers on the broiler rack. Broil 5 inches from the heat until browned and cooked through, about 4 minutes on each side.

PER SERVING (1 skewer): 179 Cal, 7 g Fat, 2 g Sat Fat, 0 g Trans Fat, 72 mg Chol, 349 mg Sod, 2 g Carb, 1 g Fib, 26 g Prot, 18 mg Calc. **POINTS** value: **4.**

☼ GOOD IDEA **These skewers are like many of the tapas, "little dishes," that are served throughout Spain. And they make a great light lunch or tempting addition to dinner. Substitute cubes of chicken or lamb for the pork, if desired.**

Spanish-Style Roast Leg of Lamb

3 garlic cloves, minced

1 tablespoon tomato paste

1 tablespoon paprika

2 teaspoons dried oregano

½ teaspoon dried thyme

1½ teaspoons salt

½ teaspoon freshly ground pepper

1 (2¼-pound) boneless leg of lamb, trimmed

4 onions, sliced

¾ cup dry sherry

HANDS-ON PREP 10 MIN
COOK 1 HR
SERVES 8

1 Preheat the oven to 400°F; spray a roasting pan with nonstick spray.

2 Combine the garlic, tomato paste, paprika, oregano, thyme, salt, and pepper in a small bowl. Rub all over the lamb.

3 Place the onions and sherry in the roasting pan; set the lamb on top. Roast until an instant-read thermometer inserted in the center of the lamb registers 145°F for medium, about 1 hour. Transfer the lamb to a cutting board and cover loosely with foil; let stand about 10 minutes. Cut into 24 slices and serve topped with the onions.

PER SERVING (3 slices lamb and 3 tablespoons onions): 240 Cal, 9 g Fat, 3 g Sat Fat, 0 g Trans Fat, 88 mg Chol, 530 mg Sod, 10 g Carb, 2 g Fib, 28 g Prot, 32 mg Calc. *POINTS* value: *5.*

☼ ZAP IT **Your microwave oven is the perfect place to reheat any leftover lamb without cooking it further. Lay 3 slices on a plate and cover with a sheet of wax paper. Microwave on Medium power until gently heated through, about 1 minute.**

SPANISH-STYLE ROAST LEG OF
LAMB WITH ROASTED PEPPERS
AND SALSA CRIOLLA, PAGE 200

Butterflied Leg of Lamb, Santa Fe–Style

½ small onion, finely chopped
3 garlic cloves, minced
1 jalapeño chile pepper, seeded and minced (wear gloves to prevent irritation)
1 tablespoon fresh lime juice
2 teaspoons curry powder
1 teaspoon chili powder
1 teaspoon dried oregano
1 (1¾-pound) butterflied boneless leg of lamb, trimmed
¾ teaspoon salt
½ teaspoon freshly ground pepper

HANDS-ON PREP 15 MIN
COOK 25 MIN
SERVES 6

1 Combine the onion, garlic, jalapeño pepper, lime juice, curry powder, chili powder, and oregano in a large bowl. Place the lamb in the bowl and rub with the onion mixture; refrigerate, covered, about 1 hour.

2 Spray the grill rack with nonstick spray; prepare the grill.

3 Sprinkle the lamb with the salt and ground pepper and place on the grill rack. Grill, covered, until an instant-read thermometer inserted in the thickest part of the lamb registers 145°F for medium, about 25 minutes. Transfer to a cutting board and cover loosely with foil; let stand about 10 minutes. Cut into 24 slices.

PER SERVING (4 slices): 213 Cal, 9 g Fat, 3 g Sat Fat, 0 g Trans Fat, 91 mg Chol, 371 mg Sod, 2 g Carb, 1 g Fib, 29 g Prot, 21 mg Calc. **POINTS** value: **5.**

✹ GOOD IDEA **Cut any leftover lamb into matchstick-thin strips and toss with some torn romaine lettuce, tomato wedges, cucumber slices, cilantro leaves, and a few red onion slices. Drizzle with a little fresh lime juice and olive oil and serve topped with 1 or 2 tablespoons shredded fat-free cheddar cheese for a quick and easy lunch.**

Chili-Rubbed Lamb Chops with Tomato-Olive Salsa

¾ teaspoon salt

½ teaspoon chili powder

½ teaspoon dried oregano

¼ teaspoon ground coriander

¼ teaspoon freshly ground pepper

4 (5-ounce) bone-in lamb loin chops, about 1-inch thick, trimmed

1 tomato, finely chopped

½ green bell pepper, seeded and finely chopped

1 small onion, finely chopped

4 small pimiento-stuffed green olives, chopped

1 tablespoon chopped fresh cilantro

1 tablespoon fresh lime juice

HANDS-ON PREP 15 MIN

COOK 10 MIN

SERVES 4

1 To make the rub, combine ½ teaspoon of the salt, the chili powder, oregano, coriander, and ⅛ teaspoon of the ground pepper in a small bowl. Rub the mixture on the lamb chops; let stand about 15 minutes.

2 Meanwhile, to make the salsa, combine the tomato, bell pepper, onion, olives, cilantro, lime juice, and the remaining ¼ teaspoon salt and ⅛ teaspoon ground pepper in a small bowl. Set aside.

3 Spray the broiler rack with nonstick spray and preheat the broiler.

4 Place the chops on the broiler rack. Broil 5 inches from the heat until an instant-read thermometer inserted in the side of the meat registers 145°F for medium, 4–5 minutes on each side. Serve with the salsa.

PER SERVING (1 lamb chop and ¼ cup salsa): 134 Cal, 6 g Fat, 2 g Sat Fat, 0 g Trans Fat, 52 mg Chol, 542 mg Sod, 3 g Carb, 1 g Fib, 17 g Prot, 18 mg Calc. *POINTS* value: *3.*

☀ GOOD IDEA **The simple spice rub and easy, colorful salsa would also work wonderfully on grilled or broiled red snapper, salmon, or shrimp.**

Roasted Lamb Chops with Mushrooms and Wine

2 teaspoons olive oil

1 onion, chopped

2 garlic cloves, minced

1 (6-ounce) package fresh white or cremini mushrooms, sliced

¾ teaspoon salt

¼ teaspoon freshly ground pepper

¾ cup dry red wine

2 tablespoons tomato paste

4 (5-ounce) bone-in lamb loin chops, about 1-inch thick, trimmed

HANDS-ON PREP 10 MIN
COOK 28 MIN
SERVES 4

1 Preheat the oven to 400°F. Spray an 8-inch square baking dish or casserole with nonstick spray.

2 Heat 1 teaspoon of the oil in a medium nonstick skillet over medium-high heat. Add the onion and garlic; cook, stirring, until softened, about 3 minutes. Add the mushrooms, ½ teaspoon of the salt and ⅛ teaspoon of the pepper; cook, stirring, until the mushrooms brown and release their liquid, about 5 minutes. Stir in ½ cup of the wine and the tomato paste; cook until the liquid is almost evaporated, about 3 minutes. Spread the mixture in the baking dish.

3 Sprinkle the lamb with the remaining ¼ teaspoon salt and ⅛ teaspoon pepper. Heat the remaining 1 teaspoon oil in the same skillet (no need to clean it) over medium-high heat. Add the lamb chops and cook until browned, about 2 minutes on each side. Place the chops on top of the mushroom mixture.

4 Add the remaining ¼ cup wine to the skillet. Cook, scraping up any browned bits from the bottom of the pan, until the wine is slightly reduced, about 1 minute. Pour the wine over the lamb and cover the dish tightly with foil. Roast until the chops are tender and cooked through, about 12 minutes. Divide the chops and mushroom mixture among 4 plates.

PER SERVING (1 lamb chop and ¼ cup mushroom mixture): 177 Cal, 8 g Fat, 2 g Sat Fat, 0 g Trans Fat, 52 mg Chol, 552 mg Sod, 8 g Carb, 1 g Fib, 18 g Prot, 22 mg Calc. *POINTS* value: *4.*

Lamb and Bell Pepper Fajitas

2 teaspoons olive oil
¾ pound boneless leg of lamb, trimmed and cut into 2 x ¼-inch strips
1 onion, sliced
1 red bell pepper, seeded and sliced
1 green bell pepper, seeded and sliced
½ teaspoon ground cumin
1 tablespoon reduced-sodium soy sauce
4 (8-inch) fat-free flour tortillas
½ cup prepared tomatillo salsa
¼ cup fat-free sour cream

HANDS-ON PREP 10 MIN
COOK 15 MIN
SERVES 4

1 Heat 1 teaspoon of the oil in a large nonstick skillet over medium-high heat. Add the lamb and cook, stirring, until browned and cooked through, about 5 minutes; transfer to a medium bowl.

2 Heat the remaining 1 teaspoon oil in the same skillet. Add the onion and bell peppers; cook, stirring occasionally, until very soft, about 6 minutes. Add the lamb and cumin; cook, stirring, about 1 minute. Stir in the soy sauce and cook until the liquid is almost evaporated, about 30 seconds. Remove from the heat.

3 Meanwhile, warm the tortillas according to the package directions. Top each tortilla with about ¾ cup of the lamb mixture, 2 tablespoons salsa, and 1 tablespoon sour cream. Fold each tortilla in half and serve at once.

PER SERVING (1 fajita): 348 Cal, 9 g Fat, 3 g Sat Fat, 0 g Trans Fat, 60 mg Chol, 694 mg Sod, 42 g Carb, 3 g Fib, 24 g Prot, 92 mg Calc. **POINTS** value: **7.**

✸ EXPRESS LANE **Planning ahead can save you kitchen time later. Slice the lamb, onion, and bell peppers several hours or up to a day ahead, and store the lamb and vegetables in separate zip-close plastic bags.**

Lamb and Brown Rice Burritos

1 cup quick-cooking
  brown rice
¾ pound boneless leg of
  lamb, trimmed and cut
  into thin strips
1 garlic clove, minced
1 tablespoon fresh lime
  juice
2 teaspoons Worcestershire
  sauce
1 teaspoon olive oil
1 onion, sliced
½ teaspoon Mexican, chili,
  or taco seasoning
½ teaspoon salt
4 (8-inch) flour tortillas
4 tablespoons fat-free sour
  cream

HANDS-ON PREP 25 MIN
COOK 10 MIN
SERVES 4

1 Cook the rice according to the package directions; keep warm.

2 Meanwhile, combine the lamb, garlic, lime juice, and Worcestershire sauce in a large bowl and toss to coat; let stand about 15 minutes.

3 Heat the oil in a medium nonstick skillet over medium-high heat. Add the lamb and cook, stirring often, until browned, about 4 minutes; transfer to a medium bowl. Add the onion to the skillet and cook, stirring, until beginning to soften, about 3 minutes. Return the lamb to the skillet along with the Mexican seasoning and salt; cook, stirring, until the lamb is cooked through, about 2 minutes.

4 Warm the tortillas according to the package directions. Put 1 tortilla on a work surface and spoon ½ cup of the rice and ½ cup of the lamb mixture down the center. Fold the short sides over the filling, then roll up jelly-roll style to enclose the filling. Repeat with the remaining tortillas, rice, and lamb mixture. Top each burrito with 1 tablespoon sour cream and serve at once.

PER SERVING (1 burrito): 398 Cal, 11 g Fat, 3 g Sat Fat, 0 g Trans Fat, 60 mg Chol, 845 mg Sod, 49 g Carb, 4 g Fib, 25 g Prot, 98 mg Calc. *POINTS* value: **8.**

✴ EXPRESS LANE **The burritos can be made several hours ahead and warmed just before serving.**

Carnitas Tostadas

1 pound boneless leg of
lamb, trimmed and cut
into 2-inch chunks
1 cup orange juice
1 cup water
2 tablespoons red-wine
vinegar
1 teaspoon dried oregano
½ teaspoon salt
¼ teaspoon freshly ground
pepper
4 (6-inch) corn tortillas
1 cup shredded romaine
lettuce
8 tablespoons prepared
fat-free salsa
8 tablespoons fat-free
shredded cheddar cheese

HANDS-ON PREP 22 MIN
COOK 1 HR 25 MIN
SERVES 4

1 Combine the lamb, orange juice, water, vinegar, and
oregano in a large nonstick skillet; bring to a boil.
Reduce the heat and simmer, covered, until the meat is
very tender, about 1 hour. Remove the skillet from the
heat; uncover and let the lamb cool in the broth about
15 minutes. Transfer the lamb to a cutting board and
discard the broth. Using 2 forks, shred the lamb.

2 Spray the same skillet with nonstick spray. Return
the lamb to the skillet. Cook over medium-high heat,
stirring often, until the meat just starts to crisp, about
3 minutes. Sprinkle with the salt and pepper.

3 Meanwhile, preheat the oven to 400°F. Lightly
spray the tortillas with nonstick spray and place in a
single layer on a baking sheet. Bake until crisp, about
9 minutes.

4 Place 1 tortilla on each of 4 plates. Top each with
2 tablespoons lettuce, a slightly rounded ⅓ cup of the
lamb, 2 tablespoons salsa, and 2 tablespoons cheese.

PER SERVING (1 tostada): 271 Cal, 9 g Fat, 3 g Sat Fat,
0 g Trans Fat, 81 mg Chol, 699 mg Sod, 17 g Carb, 2 g Fib,
30 g Prot, 185 mg Calc. *POINTS* value: *6.*

☀ TRY IT *Carnitas* (car-NEE-tahz) are small bits
of cooked meat that are cooked a second time to
crisp them. The lamb in this recipe also tastes
fabulous in tacos, tostadas, and flour tortillas, and
this technique works equally well with beef or pork.

Simply Bueno Chicken and Turkey

CHAPTER 5

RED-ROASTED CHICKEN
WITH SWEET POTATOES

Red-Roasted Chicken with Sweet Potatoes

1 lime

1 tablespoon ancho chile powder

1 tablespoon paprika

1 tablespoon dried oregano

2 garlic cloves, minced

1 teaspoon salt

1 (3½-pound) roasting chicken, without giblets

3 (10-ounce) sweet potatoes, peeled and each quartered lengthwise

HANDS-ON PREP 15 MIN
COOK 1 HR 10 MIN
SERVES 6

1 Preheat the oven to 375°F. Place the rack of a roasting pan in the pan and spray with canola nonstick spray. Lightly spray a 9 x 13-inch baking dish.

2 Grate the zest from the lime and cut the lime in half. Squeeze 1 tablespoon of juice from the lime; set the lime halves aside. Combine the lime zest and juice, chile powder, paprika, oregano, garlic, and ½ teaspoon of the salt in a small bowl and mix until a paste forms. Loosen the skin from the breasts and legs of the chicken; rub the paste under the skin. Place the lime halves in the cavity. Tuck the wings under and tie the legs. Place, breast-side up, in the roasting pan.

3 Roast the chicken on the middle oven rack until an instant-read thermometer inserted in a thigh registers 180°F, about 1 hour and 10 minutes.

4 Meanwhile, place the potatoes in the baking dish; spray with nonstick spray and sprinkle with the remaining salt. After the chicken has roasted for 30 minutes, place the potatoes on the lower oven rack; roast until tender, about 40 minutes.

5 Remove the chicken from the oven; let stand 10 minutes. Discard the lime and carve the chicken. Serve the chicken with the sweet potatoes. Discard the chicken skin before eating.

PER SERVING (⅙ of chicken and 2 potato wedges): 268 Cal, 8 g Fat, 2 g Sat Fat, 0 g Trans Fat, 81 mg Chol, 516 mg Sod, 20 g Carb, 4 g Fib, 29 g Prot, 63 mg Calc. **POINTS** value: **5.**

Hearty Chicken and Potato Stew

4 (½-pound) bone-in
chicken breast halves,
skinned
¼ teaspoon salt
⅛ teaspoon freshly ground
pepper
1 tablespoon canola oil
1 cup prepared mild,
medium, or hot fat-free
salsa
1 small red bell pepper,
seeded and chopped
1 garlic clove, minced
1 tablespoon red-wine
vinegar
2 (¾-pound) all-purpose
potatoes, peeled and cut
into ¼-inch-thick slices
8 small pitted green olives
1 tablespoon drained
capers
1 cup frozen peas, thawed

HANDS-ON PREP 10 MIN
COOK 1 HR 15 MIN
SERVES 4

1 Sprinkle the chicken with the salt and ground
pepper. Heat the oil in a Dutch oven over medium heat.
Add the chicken and cook until browned, 5–6 minutes
on each side.

2 Add the salsa, bell pepper, garlic, vinegar, and just
enough water to cover to the Dutch oven; bring to a
boil. Reduce the heat and simmer, covered, about
30 minutes. Add the potatoes, olives, and capers;
simmer, covered, until the potatoes are tender, about
20 minutes. Add the peas and cook, uncovered, until
heated through, about 2 minutes.

3 Using a slotted spoon, transfer the chicken and
potatoes to a deep large platter; keep warm. Increase
the heat to high; reduce the liquid until slightly thickened,
about 10 minutes. Spoon the liquid over the chicken
and serve at once.

PER SERVING (1 chicken breast half with ½ cup vegetables and
sauce): 421 Cal, 10 g Fat, 2 g Sat Fat, 0 g Trans Fat, 99 mg Chol,
695 mg Sod, 41 g Carb, 6 g Fib, 41 g Prot, 63 mg Calc.
POINTS value: **8.**

☼ HOW WE DID IT **To chop a bell pepper with
ease, first cut the pepper in half through the stem
end. Remove the stem, core, and seeds, then pull out
any soft white membranes that cling to the ribs.
Place a pepper half, cut side up, on the cutting board
and slice into long thin strips, then cut the strips
crosswise into small squares.**

Chicken in Red Chile Sauce with Goat Cheese

4 (½-pound) bone-in chicken breast halves, skinned
1 cup reduced-sodium chicken broth
2 dried pasilla chile peppers, seeded and broken into small pieces (wear gloves to prevent irritation)
1 chipotle chile en adobo, chopped
1 large onion, finely chopped
1 red bell pepper, seeded and chopped
3 garlic cloves, finely chopped
3 ounces soft goat cheese
Fresh cilantro leaves

HANDS-ON PREP 25 MIN
COOK 1 HR
SERVES 6

1 Place the chicken in a large deep skillet. Add just enough water to cover and bring to a boil over high heat. Reduce the heat and simmer about 15 minutes. Remove the skillet from the heat; let the chicken cool in its liquid about 20 minutes. Transfer to a cutting board. When cool enough to handle, use your fingers to finely shred the chicken or cut into long thin strips.

2 To make the chile sauce, heat the broth just to boiling in a medium saucepan. Remove the saucepan from the heat. Add the pasilla chiles and chipotle chile and soak about 30 minutes. Transfer the chile mixture to a food processor. Add the onion, bell pepper, and garlic; pulse until very finely chopped. Return to the same saucepan and simmer until heated through, about 15 minutes.

3 Meanwhile, preheat the oven to 375°F.

4 Spread 1 cup of the chile sauce on the bottom of an 8-inch square baking dish. Spread the shredded chicken over the sauce in an even layer and top with the remaining sauce. Sprinkle with the goat cheese. Cover tightly with foil. Bake 20 minutes, uncover, and bake until some of the liquid is evaporated, about 5 minutes. Sprinkle with cilantro just before serving.

PER SERVING (⅙ of casserole): 203 Cal, 7 g Fat, 3 g Sat Fat, 0 g Trans Fat, 72 mg Chol, 269 mg Sod, 7 g Carb, 1 g Fib, 28 g Prot, 50 mg Calc. **POINTS** value: **4.**

Veracruz-Style Arroz con Pollo

4 tomatoes, coarsely chopped

2 onions, coarsely chopped

2 leeks, cleaned and sliced (white and light green parts only)

1 red bell pepper, seeded and coarsely chopped

1 garlic clove, chopped

¼ teaspoon salt

¼ teaspoon freshly ground pepper

4 (¾-pound) bone-in chicken breast halves, skinned and cut crosswise in half

1 tablespoon olive oil

2 cups long-grain white rice

½ cup raisins

6 small pimiento-stuffed green olives, chopped

1 tablespoon drained capers

HANDS-ON PREP 25 MIN
COOK 55 MIN
SERVES 8

1 Put the tomatoes, onions, leeks, bell pepper, garlic, salt, and ground pepper in a food processor; pulse until finely chopped. Transfer to a Dutch oven and add the chicken. Bring to a boil over medium heat. Reduce the heat and simmer, covered, turning the chicken once, about 15 minutes.

2 Transfer the chicken to a plate and measure the liquid in the Dutch oven. Add enough water to equal 4 cups; transfer the mixture to a large bowl. Wash and dry the Dutch oven.

3 Heat the oil in the Dutch oven over medium heat. Add the rice and cook, stirring with a wooden spoon, until coated, about 30 seconds. Pour the tomato mixture over the rice; stir in the raisins, olives, and capers. Return the chicken to the pot and bring to a boil over medium heat. Reduce the heat, and simmer, covered, until the chicken is cooked through, the rice is tender, and the liquid is absorbed, about 30 minutes.

PER SERVING (1 piece chicken and 1 cup rice mixture): 422 Cal, 7 g Fat, 2 g Sat Fat, 0 g Trans Fat, 74 mg Chol, 220 mg Sod, 57 g Carb, 3 g Fib, 32 g Prot, 61 mg Calc. **POINTS** value: **8.**

✷ HOW WE DID IT **Leeks can be very sandy. Here's an easy way to clean them: Cut each leek lengthwise in half, keeping the root end intact. Wash them under cold water, making sure to get between the layers to remove all the grit.**

VERACRUZ-STYLE ARROZ
CON POLLO

Classic Arroz con Pollo

4 (½-pound) bone-in
chicken breast halves,
skinned and cut
crosswise in half
¼ teaspoon salt
¼ teaspoon freshly ground
pepper
1 tablespoon olive oil
2 onions, thinly sliced
1 garlic clove, chopped
¾ teaspoon ground cumin
4 cups reduced-sodium
chicken broth
1 (14½-ounce) can diced
tomatoes, drained
1 (4-ounce) can diced
green chiles, drained
¼ teaspoon saffron threads,
crumbled
2 cups long-grain white
rice
1 red bell pepper, seeded
and cut into thin strips

HANDS-ON PREP 10 MIN
COOK 1 HR 5 MIN
SERVES 8

1 Sprinkle the chicken with the salt and ground pepper. Heat the oil in a Dutch oven over medium heat. Add the chicken and cook in batches, turning occasionally, until browned, 8–10 minutes for each batch. Set the chicken aside.

2 Add the onions, garlic, and cumin to the Dutch oven; cook, stirring, until softened, about 5 minutes. Add the broth and cook, scraping up any browned bits in the bottom of the pan. Add the chicken, tomatoes, chiles, and saffron to the Dutch oven. Bring to a boil; reduce the heat to low and simmer, covered, about 10 minutes.

3 Stir in the rice and arrange the bell pepper strips on top. Simmer, covered, stirring once or twice, until the chicken is cooked through, the rice is tender, and the liquid is absorbed, about 30 minutes.

PER SERVING (1 piece chicken and 1 cup rice mixture): 336 Cal, 5 g Fat, 1 g Sat Fat, 0 g Trans Fat, 49 mg Chol, 509 mg Sod, 47 g Carb, 2 g Fib, 24 g Prot, 63 mg Calc. *POINTS* value: *7.*

✹ MAKE IT CORE **Use 3 cups quick-cooking brown rice instead of the 2 cups long-grain white rice and cook for 20 to 25 minutes in Step 3.**

Chicken Breasts with Bacon, Olives, and Capers

4 (½-pound) bone-in chicken breast halves, skinned
¼ teaspoon salt
¼ teaspoon freshly ground pepper
¼ teaspoon ground cumin
¼ teaspoon ground coriander
2 cups dry white wine
1 cup reduced-sodium chicken broth
¼ cup white-wine vinegar
4 slices Canadian bacon, cut into thin strips
8 small pimiento-stuffed green olives
2 tablespoons drained capers
2 tablespoons chopped fresh parsley

HANDS-ON PREP 10 MIN
COOK 45 MIN
SERVES 4

1 Sprinkle the chicken with the salt, pepper, cumin, and coriander. Spray a Dutch oven with nonstick spray and set over medium heat. Add the chicken, wine, broth, and vinegar; bring to a boil. Reduce the heat and simmer, covered, until the chicken is cooked through, about 30 minutes. Transfer the chicken to a plate; keep warm.

2 Increase the heat to high; cook until the liquid is reduced to about 2 cups, about 10 minutes. Transfer ¾ cup of the liquid to a small bowl and stir in the bacon, olives, and capers. Discard the remaining liquid or refrigerate, covered, for another use.

3 Transfer the chicken to 4 plates, spoon the bacon mixture on top, and sprinkle with the parsley.

PER SERVING (1 chicken breast half and ⅓ cup sauce): 290 Cal, 8 g Fat, 2 g Sat Fat, 0 g Trans Fat, 111 mg Chol, 927 mg Sod, 6 g Carb, 1 g Fib, 42 g Prot, 45 mg Calc. **POINTS** value: **6.**

✴ MAKE IT CORE It's easy to fit this recipe into the **Core Plan.** Substitute 2 cups of chicken broth for the wine.

Pickled Chicken and Vegetables

4 (½-pound) bone-in
chicken breast halves,
skinned
¼ teaspoon salt
1 tablespoon olive oil
2 medium red onions,
thinly sliced
2 small carrots, thinly
sliced
1 bay leaf
6 whole black peppercorns
½ cup white-wine vinegar

HANDS-ON PREP 5 MIN
COOK 45 MIN
SERVES 4

1 Sprinkle the chicken with the salt. Heat the oil in a large nonstick skillet over medium heat. Add the chicken and cook until browned, 5–6 minutes on each side. Transfer the chicken to a plate. Increase the heat to medium-high. Add the onions, carrots, bay leaf, and peppercorns; cook, stirring, until the onions are softened, about 5 minutes.

2 Return the chicken to the skillet and add the vinegar. Reduce the heat and simmer, covered, until the chicken is cooked through, about 30 minutes. Discard the bay leaf and peppercorns. Remove the skillet from the heat; let the chicken cool in the liquid to room temperature. Refrigerate until thoroughly chilled, about 3 hours.

3 Transfer the chicken to 4 plates, top with the vegetables, and serve chilled. Discard the liquid.

PER SERVING (1 chicken breast half and ¼ cup vegetables): 268 Cal, 9 g Fat, 2 g Sat Fat, 0 g Trans Fat, 99 mg Chol, 256 mg Sod, 10 g Carb, 2 g Fib, 37 g Prot, 40 mg Calc. *POINTS* value: **6.**

✺ FOOD NOTE Called *escabechado* (es-kah-beh-CHA-do) in Chile, this dish is one of the many versions of pickled chicken found throughout the Spanish-speaking world. The classic garnish is chopped pimiento, sliced tomatoes, steamed green beans, peas, and artichoke hearts—all good for followers of the **Core Plan.**

Chicken-Vegetable Platter with Tomato-Salsa Dressing

4 (¼-pound) skinless boneless chicken breast halves

¼ teaspoon salt

⅛ teaspoon freshly ground pepper

3 zucchini, thinly sliced

1 teaspoon red-wine vinegar

1 cup fresh green beans, trimmed

2 tomatoes, chopped

1 cup prepared mild, medium, or hot fat-free salsa

1 cup shredded romaine lettuce

1 Hass avocado, halved, pitted, peeled, and chopped

6 radishes, thinly sliced

4 scallions, thinly sliced

2 tablespoons chopped fresh cilantro

HANDS-ON PREP 25 MIN
COOK 25 MIN
SERVES 4

1 Sprinkle the chicken with the salt and pepper. Spray a ridged grill pan with canola nonstick spray and set over medium heat. Cook the chicken until browned and cooked through, 5–6 minutes on each side. Transfer to a plate and set aside.

2 Spray a large nonstick skillet with nonstick spray and set over medium heat. Add the zucchini and cook, stirring, until softened, about 4 minutes. Transfer the zucchini to a medium bowl and stir in the vinegar.

3 Meanwhile, cook the green beans in a medium saucepan of boiling water until crisp-tender, about 5 minutes. Drain, then rinse under cold running water. Pat the green beans dry with paper towels. Combine the tomatoes and ¼ cup of the salsa in a small bowl.

4 Arrange the chicken on a platter. Place the zucchini, green beans, and lettuce in separate piles around the chicken. Spoon the tomato mixture over the chicken and vegetables. Garnish with the avocado, radishes, scallions, and cilantro. Serve with the remaining salsa.

PER SERVING (1 chicken breast half, 1½ cups vegetables, and 3 tablespoons salsa): 277 Cal, 11 g Fat, 2 g Sat Fat, 0 g Trans Fat, 68 mg Chol, 520 mg Sod, 18 g Carb, 8 g Fib, 30 g Prot, 96 mg Calc. **POINTS** value: **6.**

✺ ZAP IT Microwaving greens beans is an easy alternative to cooking them in a saucepan. And it only takes about 5 minutes on Medium power.

ENCHILADAS SUIZAS

Enchiladas Suizas

2 pounds bone-in chicken
breast halves
25 fresh tomatillos (about
2½ pounds), husked,
rinsed, and quartered
1 jalapeño chile pepper,
halved and seeded (wear
gloves to prevent
irritation)
2 teaspoons sugar
¼ teaspoon salt
Pinch freshly ground
pepper
1 onion, finely chopped
2 garlic cloves, minced
12 (6-inch) corn tortillas
12 tablespoons shredded
reduced-fat Monterey
Jack cheese
12 tablespoons fat-free
sour cream
⅓ cup chopped fresh
cilantro

HANDS-ON PREP 25 MIN
COOK 55 MIN
SERVES 6

1 Place the chicken in a large deep skillet; add enough water to cover. Bring to a boil. Reduce the heat; simmer about 15 minutes. Remove from the heat. When cool enough to handle, shred the chicken; discard the skin and bones.

2 Preheat the oven to 350°F. Spray a 9 x 13-inch baking dish with nonstick spray. Put the tomatillos, jalapeño pepper, sugar, salt, and ground pepper in a food processor; pulse until coarsely chopped.

3 Spray a large nonstick skillet with nonstick spray and set over medium heat. Add the onion and garlic; cook, stirring, until softened, about 5 minutes. Remove from the heat and stir in the tomatillo mixture.

4 Dip both sides of 1 tortilla in the tomatillo mixture. Top with about ¼ cup of the shredded chicken, ½ tablespoon cheese, and 1 tablespoon sour cream. Fold two opposite sides of the tortilla over. Place, seam side down, in the baking dish. Repeat. Pour the remaining tomatillo mixture over the top. Sprinkle with the remaining cheese and the cilantro.

5 Cover the dish tightly with foil. Bake 20 minutes, then uncover and bake until the edges just begin to brown and the cheese is melted, about 10 minutes.

PER SERVING (2 enchiladas and ⅙ of sauce): 356 Cal, 9 g Fat, 3 g Sat Fat, 0 g Trans Fat, 73 mg Chol, 395 mg Sod, 39 g Carb, 6 g Fib, 31 g Prot, 249 mg Calc. *POINTS* value: *7*.

Grilled Chicken with Green and Red Tomato Sauce

6 (¼-pound) skinless boneless chicken breast halves

2 teaspoons dried oregano

1 teaspoon ground cumin

2 teaspoons olive oil

1 onion, chopped

2 garlic cloves, minced

1 jalapeño chile pepper, seeded and minced (wear gloves to prevent irritation)

1 (12-ounce) can tomatillos, drained and broken up

1 pint grape tomatoes, halved

3 tablespoons chopped fresh cilantro

HANDS-ON PREP 15 MIN
COOK 30 MIN
SERVES 6

1 Sprinkle the chicken with the oregano and cumin. Spray a nonstick ridged grill pan with canola nonstick spray and set over medium-high heat. Add the chicken and cook, turning occasionally, until browned and cooked through, about 12 minutes. Transfer the chicken to a serving plate; keep warm.

2 Meanwhile, heat the oil in a medium nonstick saucepan over medium-high heat. Add the onion, garlic, and jalapeño pepper; cook, stirring frequently, until the onion is golden, about 7 minutes. Add the tomatillos and simmer, stirring occasionally, about 5 minutes. Add the grape tomatoes and simmer, stirring occasionally, until softened, about 2 minutes. Stir in the cilantro. Serve the chicken with the sauce.

PER SERVING (1 chicken breast half and ¼ cup sauce): 194 Cal, 6 g Fat, 1 g Sat Fat, 0 g Trans Fat, 68 mg Chol, 117 mg Sod, 8 g Carb, 2 g Fib, 26 g Prot, 37 mg Calc. *POINTS* value: **4.**

☼ GOOD IDEA **This full-flavored dish is just as delicious served cold. So plan ahead; cook up a double batch and enjoy the tasty leftovers for a satisfying weeknight dinner.**

Chicken Breasts Verde

⅔ cup prepared fat-free
   tomatillo salsa
2 tablespoons chopped
   fresh cilantro
4 (¼-pound) skinless
   boneless chicken breast
   halves
¼ teaspoon salt
Pinch cayenne
Fresh cilantro sprigs, for
   garnish

HANDS-ON PREP 10 MIN
COOK 12 MIN
SERVES 4

1 Combine the salsa and chopped cilantro in a
small bowl.

2 Sprinkle the chicken with the salt and cayenne. Spray
a ridged grill pan with canola nonstick spray and set
over medium heat. Add the chicken and cook until the
chicken is cooked through, about 6 minutes on each
side. Transfer to a cutting board. When cool enough to
handle, cut the chicken into long thin strips.

3 Transfer the chicken to 4 plates. Top with the salsa
mixture and garnish with cilantro sprigs.

PER SERVING (1 chicken breast half and 2 rounded tablespoons
salsa): 153 Cal, 4 g Fat, 1 g Sat Fat, 0 g Trans Fat, 68 mg Chol,
328 mg Sod, 3 g Carb, 1 g Fib, 25 g Prot, 18 mg Calc.
POINTS value: **3.**

✸ GOOD IDEA **Round out the meal by serving
the chicken and salsa over brown rice (½ cup
cooked brown rice for each serving will increase
the *POINTS* value by 2).**

Sesame-Crusted Chicken Breasts with Mango-Jicama Salsa

3 tablespoons fresh lime juice

2 garlic cloves, minced

¾ teaspoon salt

¼ teaspoon crushed red pepper

4 (¼-pound) skinless boneless chicken breast halves

1 mango, pitted, peeled, and diced

½ cup peeled and diced jicama

¼ cup chopped red onion

2 tablespoons chopped fresh cilantro

¼ cup plain dried bread crumbs

2 tablespoons sesame seeds

HANDS-ON PREP 30 MIN
COOK 28 MIN
SERVES 4

1 Combine the lime juice, garlic, salt, and crushed red pepper in a small bowl. Transfer 1 tablespoon of the mixture to a serving bowl; set aside. Place the remaining lime-juice mixture in a zip-close plastic bag and add the chicken. Squeeze out the air and seal the bag; turn to coat the chicken. Refrigerate, turning the bag occasionally, at least 30 minutes or up to overnight.

2 Meanwhile, to make the salsa, add the mango, jicama, onion, and cilantro to the reserved lime-juice mixture; toss to combine. Set aside.

3 Preheat the oven to 375°F. Spray a baking sheet with nonstick spray.

4 Combine the bread crumbs and sesame seeds on a piece of wax paper. Lift the chicken from the marinade, one piece at a time, and coat on both sides with the bread-crumb mixture. Place the chicken on the baking sheet. Discard any remaining marinade and bread-crumb mixture. Spray each piece of chicken lightly with nonstick spray. Bake until lightly browned and cooked through, 28–30 minutes. Serve with the salsa.

PER SERVING (1 chicken breast half and ½ cup salsa): 238 Cal, 7 g Fat, 2 g Sat Fat, 0 g Trans Fat, 68 mg Chol, 560 mg Sod, 17 g Carb, 2 g Fib, 27 g Prot, 43 mg Calc. **POINTS** value: **5.**

✺ TRY IT *Jicama* (HI-kah-muh) is a large roundish root vegetable prized for being both sweet and crunchy.

SESAME-CRUSTED CHICKEN
BREASTS WITH MANGO-JICAMA
SALSA AND CHICKPEAS WITH
CHILES, PAGE 191

Chicken with Pumpkin Seed–Tomatillo Sauce

1 tablespoon canola oil

½ small onion, finely chopped

½ serrano or jalapeño chile pepper, seeded and finely chopped (wear gloves to prevent irritation)

1 garlic clove, chopped

2 tablespoons shelled pumpkin seeds

¼ pound tomatillos, husked, rinsed, and chopped

1 small Hass avocado, halved, pitted, peeled, and sliced

1 tablespoon chopped fresh cilantro

6 (¼-pound) skinless boneless chicken breast halves

¼ teaspoon salt

Pinch freshly ground pepper

HANDS-ON PREP 20 MIN
COOK 15 MIN
SERVES 6

1 Heat the oil in a large nonstick skillet over medium-low heat. Add the onion, serrano pepper, and garlic; cook, covered, stirring occasionally, until softened, about 5 minutes.

2 Pulse the pumpkin seeds in a food processor until finely ground; transfer to a small bowl. Puree the tomatillos and avocado in the food processor (no need to clean the bowl). Add the ground pumpkin seeds, cilantro, and onion mixture and pulse until blended.

3 Spray the grill rack with nonstick spray; prepare the grill. Sprinkle the chicken with the salt and ground pepper. Grill until the chicken is cooked through, 5–6 minutes on each side. Serve with the sauce.

PER SERVING (1 chicken breast half and 2 tablespoons sauce): 235 Cal, 12 g Fat, 2 g Sat Fat, 0 g Trans Fat, 68 mg Chol, 163 mg Sod, 5 g Carb, 2 g Fib, 27 g Prot, 21 mg Calc. *POINTS* value: *5.*

✹ MAKE IT CORE **Omit the pumpkin seeds and cut the *POINTS* value by almost *1*.**

Chicken and Avocado Tacos

4 (¼-pound) skinless
  boneless chicken breast
  halves
1 teaspoon ground cumin
¼ teaspoon salt
¼ teaspoon freshly ground
  pepper
12 (6-inch) corn tortillas
20 grape or cherry
  tomatoes, quartered
1 large Hass avocado,
  halved, pitted, peeled,
  and chopped
1 medium red onion,
  finely chopped
8 tablespoons chopped
  fresh cilantro
8 tablespoons fat-free
  sour cream
2 limes, cut into wedges

HANDS-ON PREP 25 MIN
COOK 24 MIN
SERVES 6

1 Sprinkle the chicken with the cumin, salt, and pepper. Spray a ridged grill pan with nonstick spray and set over medium heat. Cook the chicken until browned and cooked through, about 6 minutes on each side. Transfer to a cutting board. When cool enough to handle, shred the chicken or cut into long, thin strips.

2 Heat a dry medium skillet over medium heat. Warm the tortillas, one at a time, about 1 minute on each side. Stack the tortillas on a plate; keep warm.

3 Spoon ⅓ cup of the chicken onto each warm tortilla and top with about ¼ cup tomatoes, 2 tablespoons avocado, 2 tablespoons onion, 1 tablespoon cilantro, and 1 tablespoon sour cream. Fold each tortilla in half and place on a platter. Garnish the platter with the lime wedges and serve.

PER SERVING (2 tacos): 291 Cal, 9 g Fat, 2 g Sat Fat, 0 g Trans Fat, 47 mg Chol, 252 Sod, g Carb, 7 g Fib, 22 g Prot, 141 mg Calc. *POINTS* value: *6.*

☀ FOOD NOTE Did you know that avocado is really a fruit? It is, but we treat it as a vegetable since it isn't sweet. When perfectly ripe, an avocado has a lush, buttery, nutty flavor that can't be beat. Buy one that is heavy for its size and free of bruises. Store at room temperature until it yields to gentle pressure, then use at once or refrigerate up to several days.

CHIPOTLE CHICKEN
SANDWICHES WITH SALSA
MAYO AND RED ONION

Chipotle Chicken Sandwiches with Salsa Mayo and Red Onion

4 (3-ounce) skinless
   boneless chicken breast
   halves
1 teaspoon chipotle chile
   powder
½ teaspoon salt
2 tablespoons prepared
   tomato salsa
2 tablespoons reduced-fat
   mayonnaise
4 (½-inch-thick) slices
   peasant or sour dough
   bread (3½ x 6 inches)
1 cup shredded romaine
   lettuce
¼ small red onion, thinly
   sliced

HANDS-ON PREP 15 MIN
COOK 12 MIN
SERVES 4

1 Sprinkle the chicken with the chili powder and salt. Spray a large nonstick skillet with nonstick spray and set over medium-high heat. Add the chicken and cook until cooked through, about 6 minutes on each side. Transfer to a cutting board and let stand about 3 minutes, then slice on the diagonal.

2 Meanwhile, combine the salsa and mayonnaise in a cup; spread evenly on the 4 slices of bread. Layer the chicken, lettuce, and onion on each of 2 slices of the bread; top with the remaining 2 slices of bread to make 2 sandwiches. Cut each sandwich crosswise in half. Serve warm.

PER SERVING (½ sandwich): 201 Cal, 6 g Fat, 1 g Sat Fat, 0 g Trans Fat, 54 mg Chol, 578 mg Sod, 14 g Carb, 2 g Fib, 22 g Prot, 38 mg Calc. *POINTS* value: *4.*

✸ GOOD IDEA In Mexico, these sandwiches are called *tortas* and are sold everywhere. Go Mexican and serve them with radishes and roasted jalapeño peppers on the side. Use plain tomato salsa, roasted tomato salsa, chipotle salsa, or whatever salsa you happen to have on hand.

Shredded Chicken with Bell Peppers and Tomato

4 (¼-pound) skinless
boneless chicken breast
halves
¼ teaspoon salt
⅛ teaspoon cayenne
1 tablespoon olive oil
¾ teaspoon paprika
1 medium red onion, finely
chopped
½ cup finely chopped red
or yellow bell pepper
1 tomato, chopped
2 teaspoons apple-cider
vinegar
2 scallions, minced

HANDS-ON PREP 20 MIN
COOK 25 MIN
SERVES 4

1 Sprinkle the chicken with the salt and cayenne.
Spray a ridged grill pan with canola nonstick spray and
set over medium heat. Cook the chicken until browned
and cooked through, about 6 minutes on each side.
Transfer to a cutting board. When cool enough to
handle, use your fingers to shred the chicken or cut
into long, thin strips.

2 Heat the oil with the paprika in a large nonstick
skillet over medium heat. Add the onion and bell
pepper; cook, stirring, until softened, about 5 minutes.
Stir in the tomato and vinegar; cook, stirring, until the
pan is almost dry, about 3 minutes.

3 Add the chicken to the tomato mixture and cook,
stirring, until heated through, about 2 minutes.
Sprinkle with the scallions and serve.

PER SERVING (1 cup): 195 Cal, 7 g Fat, 2 g Sat Fat, 0 g Trans Fat,
68 mg Chol, 214 mg Sod, 6 g Carb, 2 g Fib, 26 g Prot, 29 mg Calc.
POINTS value: **4.**

☀ EXPRESS LANE **Save time in the kitchen by
using frozen chopped bell peppers. Or chop up a
batch of colorful bell peppers the next time you find
them on sale and freeze in zip-close freezer bags. It
will save you time and money.**

Spiced Chicken Cutlets with Orange-Avocado Salsa

- 4 (¼-pound) thinly sliced chicken breast cutlets
- 1 teaspoon ground coriander
- ½ + ⅛ teaspoon salt
- ¼ teaspoon cayenne
- 2 teaspoons olive oil
- 2 teaspoons fresh lime juice
- 1 navel orange, peeled and diced
- ½ Hass avocado, halved, pitted, peeled, and diced
- 2 scallions, thinly sliced (white and light green parts only)
- 2 tablespoons chopped fresh cilantro
- 4 lime wedges

HANDS-ON PREP 20 MIN
COOK 8 MIN
SERVES 4

1 Sprinkle the chicken with the coriander, ½ teaspoon of the salt, and the cayenne. Heat the oil in a large nonstick skillet over medium-high heat. Add the chicken and cook until browned and cooked through, about 3 minutes on each side. Transfer to a serving plate; keep warm.

2 Meanwhile, to make the salsa, combine the lime juice and the remaining ⅛ teaspoon salt in a serving bowl; stir until blended. Add the orange, avocado, scallions, and cilantro; lightly toss to coat. Serve the chicken with the salsa and the lime wedges.

PER SERVING (1 chicken cutlet and ⅓ cup salsa): 217 Cal, 9 g Fat, 2 g Sat Fat, 0 g Trans Fat, 68 mg Chol, 435 mg Sod, 7 g Carb, 3 g Fib, 26 g Prot, 41 mg Calc. **POINTS** value: **4.**

✸ GOOD IDEA To complete the meal, serve with a side of brown rice (½ cup cooked brown rice for each serving will increase the **POINTS** value by 2).

Chicken and Cremini Mushroom Fajitas

1 teaspoon ground cumin
1 teaspoon dried oregano
¾ teaspoon salt
⅛ teaspoon cayenne
¾ pound skinless boneless chicken breasts, cut into 2 x ½-inch strips
1 tablespoon olive oil
1 large onion, thinly sliced
½ pound fresh cremini or white mushrooms, sliced
¼ cup fat-free sour cream
1 teaspoon chopped drained pickled jalapeño pepper
4 (8-inch) fat-free flour tortillas
2 scallions, thinly sliced

HANDS-ON PREP 25 MIN
COOK 15 MIN
SERVES 4

1 Combine the cumin, oregano, ½ teaspoon of the salt, and the cayenne in a large bowl. Add the chicken and toss to coat; set aside about 10 minutes.

2 Meanwhile, heat the oil in a large nonstick skillet over medium-high heat. Add the onion and cook, stirring occasionally, until softened, about 5 minutes. Add the mushrooms and the remaining ¼ teaspoon salt; cook, stirring occasionally, until softened, about 3 minutes. Transfer to a plate.

3 Spray the same skillet with nonstick spray and set over medium-high heat. Add the chicken and cook, stirring occasionally, until browned and cooked through, about 5 minutes. Add the onion mixture and cook until heated through, about 1 minute.

4 Combine the sour cream and pickled jalapeño in a cup. Stack the tortillas on a microwavable plate. Cover with wax paper and microwave on High until warm, about 40 seconds. Spoon a scant 1 cup of the chicken mixture onto each tortilla. Top each with 1 tablespoon of the sour cream mixture and sprinkle with the scallions. Fold the opposite sides over to enclose the filling and serve at once.

PER SERVING (1 fajita): 327 Cal, 7 g Fat, 1 g Sat Fat, 0 g Trans Fat, 53 mg Chol, 985 mg Sod, 40 g Carb, 3 g Fib, 26 g Prot, 103 mg Calc. **POINTS** value: **7.**

I apologize for not giving this to you. Danita

CHICKEN AND CREMINI MUSHROOM FAJITAS

Chicken with Plantain and Stewed Tomatoes

2 teaspoons olive oil

1 bunch scallions, thinly sliced

2 garlic cloves, minced

4 (5- to 6-ounce) skinless bone-in chicken thighs

1 (14½-ounce) can Mexican stewed tomatoes

2 tablespoons mango chutney

1 tablespoon raisins

1 ripe plantain or firm-ripe banana, peeled and sliced

2 cups hot cooked rice

HANDS-ON PREP 10 MIN
COOK 35 MIN
SERVES 4

Heat the oil in a large nonstick skillet over medium-high heat. Add the scallions and garlic; cook, stirring frequently, until lightly browned, about 3 minutes. Add the chicken, tomatoes, chutney, and raisins; bring to a boil. Reduce the heat and simmer, covered, until the chicken is cooked through, about 25 minutes. Stir in the plantain; simmer, covered, until heated through, about 3 minutes. Serve with the rice.

PER SERVING (1 cup chicken and ½ cup rice): 402 Cal, 10 g Fat, 3 g Sat Fat, 0 g Trans Fat, 57 mg Chol, 661 mg Sod, 56 g Carb, 4 g Fib, 24 g Prot, 89 mg Calc. *POINTS* value: *8.*

✹ FOOD NOTE Mango chutney, available in supermarkets in the condiment aisle, is a great pantry item that easily adds lots of great taste to food without a lot of work. Stir some into fat-free mayonnaise and spread over toasted bread for a flavorful addition to a chicken sandwich, or serve alongside grilled or broiled salmon for dipping.

Easy Chicken Mole

4 (¼-pound) skinless
  boneless chicken thighs
½ teaspoon salt
¼ teaspoon cayenne
2 onions, thinly sliced
1 green or red bell pepper,
  seeded and thinly sliced
2 garlic cloves, minced
¾ cup reduced-sodium
  chicken broth
¼ cup prepared mild mole
  sauce
1½ tablespoons balsamic
  vinegar

HANDS-ON PREP 10 MIN
COOK 35 MIN
SERVES 4

1 Sprinkle the chicken with ¼ teaspoon of the salt and ⅛ teaspoon of the cayenne. Spray a large nonstick skillet with nonstick spray and set over medium heat. Add the chicken and cook until browned, about 4 minutes on each side. Transfer the chicken to a plate.

2 Spray the same skillet with nonstick spray and reduce the heat to medium. Add the onions, bell pepper, and garlic; cook, stirring frequently, until the onions are golden, about 10 minutes. Add the broth, mole sauce, vinegar, and the remaining ¼ teaspoon salt and ⅛ teaspoon cayenne; bring to a boil. Add the chicken; reduce the heat and simmer, covered, until cooked through, about 15 minutes.

PER SERVING (1 chicken thigh with ½ cup vegetables and sauce): 239 Cal, 11 g Fat, 3 g Sat Fat, 0 g Trans Fat, 71 mg Chol, 512 mg Sod, 9 g Carb, 2 g Fib, 26 g Prot, 53 mg Calc. *POINTS* value: *5.*

☼ TRY IT **A Mexican specialty, *mole* (MOH-lay) is a rich, dark sauce or paste made from dried chiles, nuts, spices, and chocolate. It is traditionally served with poultry and is rather time consuming to make. Store-bought mole, however, is a delicious, convenient substitute found in Hispanic markets.**

CHILI VERDE

Chili Verde

2 teaspoons canola oil

¾ pound ground skinless
chicken breast

2 garlic cloves, minced

1 bunch scallions, chopped

½ teaspoon sugar

½ teaspoon ground cumin

½ teaspoon ground
coriander

1 (15½-ounce) can
cannellini (white kidney)
beans, rinsed and drained

½ (10-ounce) package
frozen leaf spinach,
thawed

1 (12-ounce) jar
tomatillo salsa

½ cup reduced-sodium
chicken broth

¼ cup reduced-fat
sour cream

1 cup baked tortilla chips

HANDS-ON PREP 5 MIN
COOK 20 MIN
SERVES 4

1 Heat the oil in a large nonstick Dutch oven over medium-high heat. Add the chicken and garlic; cook, breaking up the chicken with a wooden spoon, until browned, about 5 minutes.

2 Set aside ¼ cup of the scallions. Add the remaining scallions, the sugar, cumin, and coriander to the Dutch oven; cook, stirring constantly, until fragrant, about 1 minute. Add the beans, spinach, salsa, and broth; bring to a boil. Reduce the heat and simmer until the flavors are blended and the chili is slightly thickened, about 10 minutes.

3 Spoon the chili into 4 bowls and top with the sour cream and reserved scallions. Serve with the tortilla chips.

PER SERVING (1 cup chili, 1 tablespoon each sour cream and scallion, and ¼ cup tortilla chips): 316 Cal, 8 g Fat, 2 g Sat Fat, 0 g Trans Fat, 57 mg Chol, 616 mg Sod, 33 g Carb, 8 g Fib, 29 g Prot, 134 mg Calc. *POINTS* value: **6.**

✸ HOW WE DID IT Ground spices lose their fragrance and flavor over time. For the freshest flavor, buy whole spices and grind them as needed in an electric coffee grinder. To clean the grinder, toss in a couple of chunks of white bread, let it whirl, then toss out the bread.

Green Chile Picadillo

2 teaspoons olive oil
1 pound ground skinless chicken breast
1 onion, chopped
2 garlic cloves, minced
1 yellow bell pepper, seeded and chopped
1 tablespoon Mexican, chili, or taco seasoning
¼ teaspoon cinnamon
1 (14½-ounce) can diced tomatoes with mild green chiles
¼ cup raisins
1 teaspoon dried oregano
¼ cup toasted sliced almonds

HANDS-ON PREP 10 MIN
COOK 20 MIN
SERVES 4

1 Heat the oil in a large nonstick skillet over medium-high heat. Add the chicken, onion, and garlic; cook, breaking up the chicken with a wooden spoon, until browned, about 8 minutes. Add the bell pepper, Mexican seasoning, and cinnamon; cook, stirring constantly, until fragrant, about 3 minutes.

2 Add the tomatoes, raisins, and oregano to the same skillet; bring to a boil. Reduce the heat and simmer, covered, until the flavors are blended, about 5 minutes. Sprinkle with the almonds and serve.

PER SERVING (generous 1 cup): 281 Cal, 9 g Fat, 2 g Sat Fat, 0 g Trans Fat, 68 mg Chol, 475 mg Sod, 23 g Carb, 3 g Fib, 28 g Prot, 84 mg Calc. **POINTS** value: **6.**

✸ EXPRESS LANE **Save some prep time by toasting up a batch of sliced almonds the next time you have a few extra minutes. Let the nuts cool and store in an airtight container at cool room temperature up to several weeks. For longer storage, freeze the nuts up to 6 months.**

Chicken Tacos with Roasted Tomato–Corn Salsa

8 taco shells
¾ pound ground skinless chicken breast
1 bunch scallions, chopped
2 garlic cloves, minced
¾ cup prepared mild roasted tomato and corn salsa
½ cup shredded romaine lettuce
8 tablespoons finely chopped tomato
8 tablespoons shredded reduced-fat pepperjack cheese

HANDS-ON PREP 15 MIN
COOK 15 MIN
SERVES 4

1 Preheat the oven to 400°F. Place the taco shells on a baking sheet. Bake until hot and crisped, about 5 minutes; keep warm.

2 Meanwhile, spray a large nonstick skillet with nonstick spray and set over medium heat. Add the chicken and cook, breaking it up with a wooden spoon, until browned, about 5 minutes. Add the scallions and garlic; cook, stirring frequently, until fragrant, about 2 minutes. Stir in the salsa and cook until heated through, about 2 minutes.

3 Spoon about ¼ cup of the chicken mixture into each taco shell. Top each with 1 tablespoon lettuce, 1 tablespoon tomato, and ½ tablespoon cheese.

PER SERVING (2 tacos): 285 Cal, 11 g Fat, 3 g Sat Fat, 0 g Trans Fat, 56 mg Chol, 403 mg Sod, 24 g Carb, 4 g Fib, 24 g Prot, 149 mg Calc. *POINTS* value: **6.**

✷ EXPRESS LANE Shredded lettuce is a great convenience food to have on hand for sprinkling into a favorite sandwich or for tossing into a fresh salad. To prepare it ahead, shred some firm lettuce, such as romaine or iceberg, roll up loosely in paper towels, and pack into a zip-close plastic bag. It will keep for several days. Just be sure to replace the towel if it gets too wet.

Oaxacan Chicken and Chickpea Stew

2 teaspoons olive oil
1 large onion, chopped
3 garlic cloves, minced
1 pound skinless boneless chicken breasts, cut into 1½-inch pieces
1 tablespoon Mexican, chili, or taco seasoning
1 small jicama, peeled and chopped (about 2 cups)
1 cup reduced-sodium chicken broth
2 (15-ounce) cans chickpeas, rinsed and drained
2 tablespoons cornmeal
¼ teaspoon salt
¼ cup chopped fresh cilantro
4 lime wedges

HANDS-ON PREP 15 MIN
COOK 23 MIN
SERVES 6

1 Heat the oil in a nonstick Dutch oven over medium-high heat. Add the onion and garlic; cook, stirring frequently, until lightly browned, about 6 minutes. Add the chicken and Mexican seasoning; cook, stirring occasionally, about 3 minutes.

2 Add the jicama and broth to the Dutch oven; bring to a boil. Reduce the heat and simmer, covered, stirring occasionally, until the chicken is cooked through, about 7 minutes. Add the chickpeas, then stir in the cornmeal and salt. Return to a boil over high heat, stirring constantly. Reduce the heat to medium and cook until slightly thickened, about 1 minute. Stir in the cilantro. Serve with the lime wedges.

PER SERVING (scant 1 cup): 321 Cal, 7 g Fat, 1 g Sat Fat, 0 g Trans Fat, 46 mg Chol, 449 mg Sod, 39 g Carb, 10 g Fib, 27 g Prot, 81 mg Calc. *POINTS* value: **6.**

✱ FOOD NOTE Store-bought Mexican seasoning, chili seasoning, and taco seasoning are convenient fast flavor fixes. They come in 1- to 2-ounce envelopes and can be found in the ethnic foods section of most supermarkets. Use whichever is your favorite blend.

FRESH CHILE PEPPERS

Chiles come in dozens of varieties and degrees of heat and are the basis of Latin American cooking. Rich in vitamins and low in calories, they provide flavor as well as heat, which is contributed by a chemical known as capsaicin. Be sure to always wear surgical gloves when handling fresh chile peppers, as they can cause irritation to the skin. Here are some of the most popular fresh chiles:

HABANERO This lantern-shaped pepper is the hottest chile grown anywhere in the world. Its color ranges from green to orange to red (when ripe) and can be eaten raw or cooked. Add a little to a dish when you want some hefty heat.

HUNGARIAN WAX Long and yellow or orange, this medium-hot chile is great pickled or raw in salads. This chile can be substituted for serranos.

JALAPEÑO Probably the most popular chile in the U.S., this thick-fleshed pepper can be added to almost any dish, raw or cooked. It is the chile that gives most salsas their heat. When ripe, this green chile turns bright red.

POBLANO This is perhaps the most useful of all the chiles. Shaped like an oblong bell pepper, it is generally roasted or stuffed to make chile rellenos.

SERRANO A slim, rather small chile that packs quite a wallop. It has a clean, biting heat. You can seed and devein it if you want a slightly less incendiary flavor.

Chicken, Tomato, and Tortilla Stew

6 (6-inch) corn tortillas,
  each cut into 6 wedges
5 tomatoes, chopped
4 serrano or jalapeño chile
  peppers, seeded and
  chopped (wear gloves to
  prevent irritation)
1 small onion, chopped
2 garlic cloves, peeled
¼ teaspoon salt
6 tablespoons chopped
  fresh cilantro
2 cups shredded cooked
  chicken breast
½ cup fat-free sour cream

HANDS-ON PREP 20 MIN
COOK 28 MIN
SERVES 4

1 Arrange the oven racks in the middle and lower third of the oven. Preheat the oven to 375°F. Place the tortillas in a single layer on 2 large baking sheets; bake until crisp, about 20 minutes.

2 Meanwhile, combine the tomatoes, serrano peppers, onion, garlic, and salt in a large saucepan and set over medium heat. Cook, stirring, until softened, about 12 minutes. Add 2 tablespoons of the cilantro and cook 1 minute. Transfer to a food processor and puree.

3 Pour the tomato mixture into a large nonstick skillet and set over medium heat. Stir in the tortillas, chicken, and 2 tablespoons of the cilantro. Cook, stirring the mixture and turning the tortillas until moistened and chewy, about 8 minutes. Spoon the chicken mixture onto a serving platter and top with dollops of the sour cream. Sprinkle with the remaining 2 tablespoons cilantro and serve.

PER SERVING (1 cup): 261 Cal, 4 g Fat, 1 g Sat Fat, 0 g Trans Fat, 60 mg Chol, 309 mg Sod, 31 g Carb, 5 g Fib, 26 g Prot, 135 mg Calc. **POINTS** value: **5.**

GOOD IDEA **Stack the tortillas on top of each other and cut them into wedges all at once. Be sure to use a sharp large chef's knife for the cleanest cuts. For the most flavor, during the summer use vine-ripened tomatoes or tomatoes from your local farmers' market.**

Black Bean, Chicken, and Roasted Corn Stew

2 teaspoons olive oil

1 large onion, chopped

2 cups shredded cooked chicken

1 (15-ounce) can black beans, rinsed and drained

2 cups fresh or thawed frozen corn kernels

¾ cup prepared fat-free chipotle chile salsa

1 cup cherry tomatoes, halved

¼ cup chopped fresh cilantro

2 tablespoons fresh lime juice

HANDS-ON PREP 15 MIN
COOK 12 MIN
SERVES 4

1 Heat the oil in a large nonstick saucepan over medium-high heat. Add the onion and cook, stirring frequently, until lightly browned, about 5 minutes. Reduce the heat and add the chicken, beans, corn, and salsa. Cook, stirring occasionally, until heated through, about 3 minutes.

2 Stir in the cherry tomatoes and cook until heated through, about 2 minutes. Stir in the cilantro and lime juice and spoon into a serving bowl.

PER SERVING (1⅓ cups): 350 Cal, 8 g Fat, 2 g Sat Fat, 0 g Trans Fat, 60 mg Chol, 553 mg Sod, 42 g Carb, 9 g Fib, 29 g Prot, 92 mg Calc. *POINTS* value: *7.*

✸ FOOD NOTE To make this dish especially tasty, use frozen roasted corn kernels, which is available in specialty food stores.

Roasted Pepper and Chicken Quesadillas

1 cup shredded reduced-fat
Mexican cheese blend
4 (9-inch) whole-wheat
flour tortillas
1 cup shredded cooked
chicken
1 cup chopped thawed
frozen or 1 (7-ounce) jar
roasted bell peppers,
drained and chopped
4 scallions, chopped
3 tablespoons chopped
fresh cilantro
2 teaspoons olive oil

HANDS-ON PREP 15 MIN
COOK 9 MIN
SERVES 4

1 Sprinkle ½ cup of the cheese on 2 of the tortillas, then top with all of the chicken, bell peppers, scallions, cilantro, and the remaining ½ cup cheese. Top with the remaining 2 tortillas, lightly pressing down on each stack.

2 Heat 1 teaspoon of the oil in a large nonstick skillet over medium heat. Add one of the tortilla stacks and cook until lightly browned and heated through, 2–3 minutes on each side. Transfer the quesadilla to a cutting board and keep warm. Repeat with the remaining 1 teaspoon oil and tortilla stack. Cut each quesadilla into 6 wedges and serve at once.

PER SERVING (3 wedges): 284 Cal, 11 g Fat, 4 g Sat Fat, 0 g Trans Fat, 40 mg Chol, 455 mg Sod, 26 g Carb, 4 g Fib, 22 g Prot, 277 mg Calc. *POINTS* value: **6.**

☼ GOOD IDEA **Crispy quesadillas are the Mexican version of a grilled cheese sandwich. Three wedges are perfect when you're looking for something quick yet a little different for lunch. And one wedge makes a tasty pre-dinner appetizer. If you like, use shredded reduced-fat cheddar cheese or pepperjack instead of the Mexican cheese blend.**

Chicken and Pepperjack Tortilla Casserole

2 teaspoons olive oil

1 onion, chopped

2 garlic cloves, minced

2 cups chopped cooked chicken

1 (10-ounce) can mild enchilada sauce

1 teaspoon dried oregano

4 (6-inch) corn tortillas, halved

½ cup shredded reduced-fat pepperjack cheese

HANDS-ON PREP 20 MIN
COOK 30 MIN
SERVES 4

1 Preheat the oven to 375°F. Spray an 8-inch square baking dish with nonstick spray.

2 Heat the oil in a large nonstick skillet over medium-high heat. Add the onion and garlic; cook, stirring frequently, until lightly browned, about 5 minutes. Add the chicken, enchilada sauce, and oregano; bring to a simmer. Remove the skillet from the heat.

3 Place 4 of the tortilla halves in an overlapping layer in the bottom of the dish. Spoon half of the chicken mixture on top and sprinkle with ¼ cup of the cheese. Repeat the layering one more time.

4 Cover the dish tightly with foil and bake about 15 minutes. Remove the foil and bake until heated through and the cheese is melted, about 5 minutes. Let stand about 5 minutes, then cut into 4 portions and serve at once.

PER SERVING (¼ of casserole): 278 Cal, 11 g Fat, 4 g Sat Fat, 0 g Trans Fat, 70 mg Chol, 525 mg Sod, 19 g Carb, 3 g Fib, 26 g Prot, 186 mg Calc. *POINTS* value: *6.*

✹ **EXPRESS LANE** This casserole is layered much like a classic lasagna and is every bit as tasty. Assemble it up to several hours ahead, then refrigerate until ready to put into the oven. Allow a little extra baking time or set the casserole out on the counter for about 1 hour so it has time to warm up a bit before being baked.

Tequila Turkey with Lime and Cilantro

4 (¼-pound) turkey
  breast cutlets
1 tablespoon Mexican,
  chili, or taco seasoning
1 tablespoon extra-virgin
  olive oil
1 onion, thinly sliced
1 red bell pepper, seeded
  and cut into thin strips
2 (15-ounce) cans yellow
  or white hominy, rinsed
  and drained
½ cup reduced-sodium
  chicken broth
2 tablespoons tequila
1 teaspoon grated lime
  zest
¼ teaspoon salt
2 tablespoons chopped
  fresh cilantro
4 lime wedges

HANDS-ON PREP 15 MIN
COOK 15 MIN
SERVES 4

1 Place the turkey cutlets between 2 sheets of plastic wrap or wax paper; gently pound to scant ¼-inch thickness with a meat mallet or heavy saucepan. Sprinkle the chicken with the Mexican seasoning.

2 Heat the oil in a large nonstick skillet over medium-high heat. Add the cutlets and cook until browned and cooked through, about 3 minutes on each side. Transfer the cutlets to a plate.

3 Set the same skillet over medium-high heat. Add the onion and bell pepper; cook, stirring frequently, until softened, about 3 minutes. Add the hominy, broth, tequila, lime zest, and salt; bring to a boil. Reduce the heat and add the turkey; simmer, covered, until heated through, about 1 minute. Sprinkle with the cilantro and serve with the lime wedges.

PER SERVING (1 turkey cutlet with about ½ cup vegetables and sauce): 310 Cal, 6 g Fat, 1 g Sat Fat, 0 g Trans Fat, 75 mg Chol, 719 mg Sod, 30 g Carb, 6 g Fib, 30 g Prot, 51 mg Calc. *POINTS* value: **6.**

✸ MAKE IT CORE **Omit the tequila to make this recipe Core Plan.**

Chunky Turkey Chili with Lentils

1½ cups lentils, picked over, rinsed, and drained

3 cups reduced-sodium chicken broth

2 teaspoons dried oregano

1 pound ground skinless turkey breast

2 carrots, diced

1 onion, chopped

2 garlic cloves, chopped

1 (14½-ounce) can diced tomatoes

1 tablespoon chili powder

1 tablespoon paprika

2 teaspoons light molasses or sugar

½ teaspoon salt

⅓ cup finely chopped red onion

¼ cup chopped fresh cilantro

HANDS-ON PREP 15 MIN
COOK 35 MIN
SERVES 6

1 Combine the lentils, broth, and oregano in a medium saucepan; bring to a boil. Reduce the heat and simmer, covered, about 10 minutes. Uncover and simmer until most of the liquid is evaporated, about 10 minutes.

2 Meanwhile, spray a large nonstick skillet with nonstick spray and set over medium-high heat. Add the turkey and cook, breaking it up with a wooden spoon, until browned, about 5 minutes. Add the carrots, onion, and garlic; cook, stirring constantly, until the onion is softened, about 6 minutes. Add the tomatoes, chili powder, paprika, molasses, and salt; bring to a boil. Reduce the heat and simmer until the flavors are blended and the chili is slightly thickened, about 20 minutes. Divide the lentils among 6 bowls. Spoon the chili on top and sprinkle with the red onion and cilantro.

PER SERVING (¾ cup chili and ½ cup lentils): 291 Cal, 2 g Fat, 0 g Sat Fat, 0 g Trans Fat, 50 mg Chol, 626 mg Sod, 38 g Carb, 11 g Fib, 33 g Prot, 95 mg Calc. *POINTS* value: **5.**

✸ MAKE IT CORE Molasses (or sugar) rounds out the flavor of this chili, but you can easily leave it out if you're following the **Core Plan.**

Fresh and
Fabulous Fish

CHAPTER 6

Salmon with Guacamole and Pico de Gallo

1 large tomato, seeded and chopped
¼ cup finely chopped onion
¼ cup chopped fresh cilantro
1 serrano chile pepper, seeded and finely chopped (wear gloves to prevent irritation)
1 garlic clove, minced
1 teaspoon + 2 tablespoons fresh lime juice
Salt
6 (¼-pound) salmon steaks
2 teaspoons canola oil
¼ teaspoon grated lime zest
Pinch freshly ground pepper
½ recipe Four-Ingredient Guacamole (page 16)

HANDS-ON PREP 20 MIN
COOK 6 MIN
SERVES 6

1 To make the pico de gallo, combine the tomato, onion, cilantro, serrano pepper, garlic, 1 teaspoon of the lime juice, and ⅛ teaspoon salt in a medium bowl.

2 Spray the broiler rack with nonstick spray; preheat the broiler.

3 Drizzle the salmon steaks with the remaining 2 tablespoons lime juice and the oil. Sprinkle with ¼ teaspoon salt, the lime zest, and ground pepper. Place the salmon on the broiler rack. Broil, 5 inches from the heat, until the salmon is just opaque in the center, 3–4 minutes on each side. Serve with the guacamole and pico de gallo. Remove the salmon skin before eating.

PER SERVING (1 salmon steak, 2 tablespoons guacamole, and 2½ tablespoons pico de gallo): 210 Cal, 11 g Fat, 2 g Sat Fat, 0 g Trans Fat, 63 mg Chol, 309 mg Sod, 6 g Carb, 3 g Fib, 22 g Prot, 23 mg Calc. *POINTS* value: *5.*

☀ TRY IT Mexican *pico de gallo* (PEE-koh deh Guy-yoh) is great with fajitas, tacos, baked tortilla chips, beans, and grilled meat or poultry. Easily doubled or tripled, this speedy relish is best made just before serving; it does not improve upon standing. If you like more heat rather than less, don't seed the serrano peppers.

SALMON WITH GUACAMOLE AND
PICO DE GALLO AND MASHED
POTATOES WITH TOMATILLO
SALSA, PAGE 195

Broiled Salmon with Chipotle Cream

½ cup fat-free sour cream
1 chipotle en adobo, seeded and chopped
2 scallions, thinly sliced
4 (6-ounce) salmon steaks, 1 inch thick
1 tablespoon fresh lime juice
2 teaspoons canola oil
Pinch salt
Pinch freshly ground pepper

HANDS-ON PREP 10 MIN
COOK 10 MIN
SERVES 4

1 To make the chipotle cream, combine the sour cream, chipotle en adobo, and half of the scallions in a small bowl. Set aside.

2 Spray the broiler rack with nonstick spray; preheat the broiler.

3 Meanwhile, drizzle the salmon with the lime juice and oil and sprinkle with the salt and ground pepper. Place the salmon on the broiler rack. Broil, 5 inches from the heat, until the salmon is just opaque in the center, about 5 minutes on each side.

4 Transfer the salmon to plates. Top with the chipotle cream and sprinkle with the remaining scallion. Remove the salmon skin before eating.

PER SERVING (1 salmon steak and about 2 tablespoons chipotle cream): 254 Cal, 11 g Fat, 3 g Sat Fat, 0 g Trans Fat, 98 mg Chol, 312 mg Sod, 6 g Carb, 0 g Fib, 32 g Prot, 62 mg Calc. *POINTS* value: **6.**

✺ MAKE IT CORE Substitute ½ teaspoon chipotle chile powder for the chipotle en adobo. Either way, you can jazz up the chipotle cream with some chopped fresh cilantro, a splash of fresh lime juice, or a sprinkling of grated lime zest. You can also substitute plain fat-free yogurt for the sour cream if you prefer.

Grilled Salmon with Pickled Onions

2 small red onions, thinly
sliced
⅔ cup apple-cider vinegar
2 garlic cloves, halved
½ teaspoon + pinch freshly
ground pepper
½ teaspoon ground
coriander
½ teaspoon ground cumin
¼ teaspoon salt
4 (6-ounce) salmon steaks,
1 inch thick
2 teaspoons canola oil
1 tablespoon chopped
fresh cilantro

HANDS-ON PREP 15 MIN
COOK 25 MIN
SERVES 4

1 To make the pickled onions, combine the onions and just enough water to cover in a large saucepan and bring to a boil; boil 1 minute. Drain in a colander and rinse under cold running water; drain again. Return the onions to the saucepan. Add the vinegar, garlic, ½ teaspoon of the pepper, the coriander, cumin, salt, and just enough water to cover; bring to a boil. Boil about 3 minutes. Transfer the onion mixture to a medium nonreactive bowl. Let stand until the flavors are blended, at least 3 hours or up to 24 hours.

2 Spray the broiler rack with nonstick spray; preheat the broiler.

3 Drizzle the salmon with the oil. Sprinkle with the remaining pinch pepper and place on the broiler rack. Broil, 5 inches from the heat, until the salmon is just opaque in the center, about 5 minutes on each side.

4 Meanwhile, remove the garlic from the pickled onions; discard. Stir in the cilantro.

5 Transfer the salmon to plates. Using a slotted spoon, top the salmon with the pickled onions. Remove the salmon skin before eating.

PER SERVING (1 salmon steak and ¼ cup pickled onions): 243 Cal, 11 g Fat, 3 g Sat Fat, 0 g Trans Fat, 95 mg Chol, 124 mg Sod, 4 g Carb, 1 g Fib, 31 g Prot, 28 mg Calc.
POINTS value: **6.**

Baked Tuna with Marjoram and Lime

2 (6-ounce) tuna steaks,
   1 inch thick
Pinch salt
1 small tomato, chopped
½ teaspoon fresh marjoram
   leaves or pinch dried
   marjoram, crumbled
2 tablespoons fresh
   lime juice

HANDS-ON PREP 10 MIN
COOK 13 MIN
SERVES 2

1 Preheat the oven to 400°F. Spray an 8-inch square baking dish with nonstick spray.

2 Place the tuna steaks in the baking dish in a single layer and sprinkle with the salt. Top with the tomato and marjoram and drizzle with the lime juice. Add just enough water to cover the bottom of the dish (about ¼ cup). Cover the baking dish tightly with foil. Bake until the tuna is slightly pink in the center, 13–15 minutes.

PER SERVING (1 tuna steak): 302 Cal, 9 g Fat, 3 g Sat Fat, 0 g Trans Fat, 101 mg Chol, 238 mg Sod, 3 g Carb, 1 g Fib, 33 g Prot, 25 mg Calc. **POINTS** value: **7.**

✴ FOOD NOTE **If you like, top the tuna steaks with fresh thyme, mint, parsley, or basil instead of the marjoram.**

Baked Red Snapper in Coconut Milk

2 cups reduced-sodium chicken broth

2 bay leaves

¼ teaspoon salt

¼ teaspoon freshly ground pepper

1 medium red onion, sliced

1 small yellow bell pepper, seeded and cut into strips

2 (½-pound) red snapper fillets, skinned and cut crosswise in half

½ cup coconut milk

1 tomato, chopped

HANDS-ON PREP 15 MIN
COOK 55 MIN
SERVES 4

1 Combine the broth, bay leaves, salt, and ground pepper in a large saucepan; bring to a boil. Reduce the heat and simmer about 10 minutes. Add the onion and bell pepper; increase the heat and cook until the flavors are blended, about 5 minutes. Transfer to a bowl. Discard the bay leaves; let cool to room temperature.

2 Meanwhile, preheat the oven to 350°F. Spray a 7 x 11-inch baking dish with nonstick spray.

3 Place the snapper fillets in the baking dish in a single layer; pour in the broth mixture and coconut milk. Cover the dish tightly with foil and bake about 15 minutes. Sprinkle with the tomato and bake, covered, about 15 minutes longer. Uncover and bake until the fish is just opaque in the center, about 5 minutes longer.

PER SERVING (½ fillet, ⅓ cup vegetables, and 3 tablespoons sauce): 188 Cal, 7 g Fat, 5 g Sat Fat, 0 g Trans Fat, 60 mg Chol, 534 mg Sod, 8 g Carb, 2 g Fib, 24 g Prot, 37 mg Calc. *POINTS* value: *4.*

☀ GOOD IDEA **A side of fluffy rice would be ideal to soak up all the delicious coconut-scented sauce (½ cup cooked brown or white rice will increase the per-serving *POINTS* value by 2).**

PERUVIAN TUNA SEVICHE
WITH WATERMELON AGUA
FRESCA, PAGE 219

Peruvian Tuna Seviche

1 pound tuna steak, cut
into ½-inch dice
¼ teaspoon salt
1 small red onion, finely
chopped
6 tablespoons fresh lime
juice
1 jalapeño chile pepper,
seeded and finely
chopped (wear gloves
to prevent irritation)
2 teaspoons canola oil
4 cups mixed baby salad
greens
4 plum tomatoes, halved
lengthwise and sliced
2 tablespoons chopped
unsalted dry-roasted
peanuts

HANDS-ON PREP 15 MIN
COOKS NONE
SERVES 4

1 Put the tuna in a medium bowl and sprinkle with
the salt. Add the onion, lime juice, jalapeño pepper,
and oil; mix well. Cover the bowl with plastic wrap and
refrigerate until the tuna is just opaque in the center,
about 5 hours.

2 Divide the greens among 4 plates. Top each with
⅓ cup of the tuna mixture, one-fourth of tomatoes, and
½ tablespoon peanuts. Serve at once.

PER SERVING (1 plate): 252 Cal, 10 g Fat, 2 g Sat Fat,
0 g Trans Fat, 43 mg Chol, 218 mg Sod, 11 g Carb, 3 g Fib,
30 g Prot, 56 mg Calc. *POINTS* value: **5.**

✿ PLAY IT SAFE When food shopping, make
fresh fish the last item you put into your cart. As
soon as you arrive home, place it in the coldest part
of the refrigerator, which is usually the back. Use
the fish within 1 day.

Cold Snapper in Spicy Vinegar Sauce

3 (½-pound) red snapper fillets, skinned and cut crosswise in half

¼ cup fresh lime juice

¼ teaspoon salt

¼ teaspoon freshly ground pepper

1 tablespoon canola oil

1 medium red onion, thinly sliced

1 cup apple-cider vinegar

2 jalapeño chile peppers, seeded and cut into thin strips (wear gloves to prevent irritation)

2 bay leaves

½ teaspoon ground cumin

¼ teaspoon ground allspice

6 cups shredded romaine lettuce

HANDS-ON PREP 20 MIN
COOK 12 MIN
SERVES 6

1 Place the snapper fillets in a 9 x 13-inch baking dish in a single layer and drizzle with the lime juice. Refrigerate, covered, turning twice, about 30 minutes.

2 Meanwhile, spray the broiler rack with nonstick spray; preheat the broiler. Sprinkle the fillets with the salt and ground pepper and place on the broiler rack. Broil, 6 inches from the heat, until the fish is just opaque in the center, 4–5 minutes.

3 Meanwhile, wash and dry the baking dish. Place the fish in the dish in a single layer. Heat the oil in a medium nonstick skillet over medium heat. Add the onion and cook, stirring, until softened, about 5 minutes. Add the vinegar, jalapeño peppers, bay leaves, cumin, and allspice; bring to a simmer. Pour the marinade over the fish; cover and refrigerate at least 2 hours or up to overnight.

4 Discard the bay leaves from the marinade. Divide the lettuce among 6 plates. With a slotted spatula, place a piece of fish on top of each pile of lettuce. Serve at once.

PER SERVING (½ fillet and 1 cup lettuce): 121 Cal, 2 g Fat, 0 g Sat Fat, 0 g Trans Fat, 60 mg Chol, 193 mg Sod, 3 g Carb, 1 g Fib, 22 g Prot, 26 mg Calc. *POINTS* value: *2.*

✺ FOOD NOTE Known as *escabeche* (es-ka-BAY-chay) in Spain, this dish is especially popular during the summer.

Cuban-Style Red Snapper with Queso Fresco

1 (8-ounce) can tomato
 sauce
2 (½-pound) red snapper
 fillets, skinned and cut
 crosswise in half
⅛ teaspoon freshly ground
 pepper
¼ cup shredded queso
 fresco
1 tablespoon chopped
 fresh parsley

HANDS-ON PREP 10 MIN
COOK 20 MIN
SERVES 4

1 Preheat the oven to 350°F.

2 Spread half of the tomato sauce in a 7 x 11-inch baking dish; place the snapper fillets on top in a single layer. Sprinkle the snapper with the pepper, then spoon the remaining tomato sauce on top; sprinkle with the cheese. Cover the dish tightly with foil. Bake until the fillets are just opaque in the center, about 20 minutes. Serve sprinkled with the parsley.

PER SERVING (½ fillet and about 3 tablespoons sauce): 146 Cal, 3 g Fat, 1 g Sat Fat, 0 g Trans Fat, 64 mg Chol, 402 mg Sod, 4 g Carb, 1 g Fib, 23 g Prot, 39 mg Calc. *POINTS* value: **3.**

✹ MAKE IT CORE If you're following the **Core Plan**, substitute an equal amount of shredded fat-free mozzarella cheese for the mild-tasting *queso fresco* (KAY-soh FRAY-skoh).

Snapper with Chipotle-Thyme Sauce

1 tablespoon olive oil

1 medium red onion, thinly sliced

1 garlic clove, minced

15 cherry tomatoes, halved

1 chipotle en adobo, seeded and chopped

¼ teaspoon dried thyme, crumbled

¼ teaspoon salt

⅛ teaspoon freshly ground pepper

2 (½-pound) red snapper fillets, skinned and cut crosswise in half

½ cup reduced-fat sour cream

HANDS-ON PREP 15 MIN
COOK 27 MIN
SERVES 4

1 Preheat the oven to 350°F. Spray a 7 x 11-inch baking dish with nonstick spray.

2 To make the sauce, heat the oil in a large nonstick skillet over medium heat. Add the onion and garlic; cook, stirring occasionally, until softened, about 5 minutes. Add the cherry tomatoes, chipotle en adobo, thyme, salt, and pepper; cook, stirring occasionally, until softened, about 2 minutes. Transfer the tomato mixture to a bowl and let cool to room temperature.

3 Place the snapper fillets in the baking dish in a single layer; top evenly with the sauce. Cover the dish tightly with foil. Bake until the fillets are just opaque in the center, about 20 minutes. Divide the fish and sauce among 4 plates and garnish each serving with a dollop of the sour cream.

PER SERVING (½ fillet, about ¼ cup sauce, and 2 tablespoons sour cream): 202 Cal, 9 g Fat, 3 g Sat Fat, 0 g Trans Fat, 72 mg Chol, 368 mg Sod, 7 g Carb, 2 g Fib, 23 g Prot, 64 mg Calc. **POINTS** value: **4.**

☀ ZAP IT **Our somewhat fiery tomato and chipotle sauce is also very tasty served over grilled chicken breasts and thinly sliced grilled flank steak. Make a double batch of the sauce and refrigerate half in an airtight container up to 4 days. To serve, transfer the sauce to a microwavable bowl, cover with a vented piece of plastic wrap, and microwave on High until just warmed through, about 2 minutes.**

Slow-Cooked Striped Bass with Vegetables

1 tablespoon olive oil
1 teaspoon ground
annatto seeds
2 large onions, finely
chopped
2 large tomatoes, chopped
2 jalapeño chile peppers,
seeded and finely
chopped (wear gloves to
prevent irritation)
2 garlic cloves, minced
½ teaspoon dried oregano,
crumbled
¼ teaspoon salt
¼ teaspoon freshly ground
pepper
2 (½-pound) striped bass
fillets, skinned and cut
crosswise in half
Juice of 1 lemon

HANDS-ON PREP 15 MIN
COOK 35 MIN
SERVES 4

1 Heat the oil in a Dutch oven over low heat. Add the annatto seeds and cook, stirring occasionally, until fragrant and deepened in color, about 5 minutes. Remove the Dutch oven from the heat.

2 Combine the onions, tomatoes, jalapeño peppers, garlic, oregano, salt, and ground pepper in a medium bowl. Spread half of the onion mixture in the bottom of the Dutch oven. Place the bass fillets on top in a single layer, then cover with the remaining onion mixture. Drizzle with the lemon juice.

3 Cook, covered, over low heat, until the vegetables are softened and the fish is just opaque in the center, about 30 minutes.

PER SERVING (½ fillet and ½ cup vegetables): 222 Cal, 8 g Fat, 2 g Sat Fat, 0 g Trans Fat, 57 mg Chol, 221 mg Sod, 13 g Carb, 3 g Fib, 24 g Prot, 62 mg Calc. **POINTS** value: **5.**

✹ TRY IT Ground *annatto* (uh-NAH-toh), a derivative of brick-colored achiote seeds, is often used in Latin American cooking to mildly season and add color to dishes. It is usually found in the spice aisle in supermarkets, but if you can't find it substitute paprika, or buy annatto seeds and grind them in a spice grinder.

Fish Tacos with Tomatillo Salsa

1 teaspoon ground cumin

1 teaspoon chili powder

¼ teaspoon salt

⅛ teaspoon freshly ground pepper

2 (6-ounce) red snapper fillets

1 tablespoon fresh lime juice

2 teaspoons olive oil

8 (6-inch) corn tortillas

½ cup prepared tomatillo salsa

2 tablespoons chopped fresh cilantro

2 tablespoons chopped red onion

HANDS-ON PREP 20 MIN
COOK 15 MIN
SERVES 4

1 Preheat the oven to 450°F. Spray a 7 x 11-inch baking dish with nonstick spray.

2 Combine the cumin, chili powder, salt, and pepper in a small bowl. Sprinkle the spice mixture on both sides of the snapper fillets. Place, skin side down, in the baking dish; drizzle with the lime juice and oil. Cover the baking dish tightly with foil and bake the fish until just opaque in the center, about 10 minutes.

3 Meanwhile, warm the tortillas according to the package directions.

4 Transfer the fillets to a cutting board; remove the skin and slice into long, thin strips. Top each tortilla with about ¼ cup of the fish, 1 tablespoon salsa, 1 generous teaspoon cilantro, and 1 generous teaspoon onion. Fold each taco in half and serve at once.

PER SERVING (2 tacos): 222 Cal, 5 g Fat, 1 g Sat Fat, 0 g Trans Fat, 45 mg Chol, 331 mg Sod, 26 g Carb, 4 g Fib, 19 g Prot, 108 mg Calc. **POINTS** value: **4.**

☀ GOOD IDEA **When serving these zesty tacos, be sure to put out small bowls of extra salsa, cilantro, and chopped red onion so family members or guests can help themselves to more.**

**FISH TACOS WITH
TOMATILLO SALSA**

Sea Bass Smothered with Shrimp

½ pound medium shrimp,
    unpeeled
1 small onion, finely
    chopped
2 garlic cloves, minced
1 large tomato, chopped
½ cup dry white wine
2 jalapeño chile peppers,
    seeded and finely
    chopped (wear gloves to
    prevent irritation)
1 teaspoon fresh oregano
    leaves or ½ teaspoon
    dried, crumbled
¼ teaspoon salt
⅛ teaspoon freshly ground
    pepper
2 (½-pound) sea bass
    fillets, skinned and cut
    crosswise in half

HANDS-ON PREP 20 MIN
COOK 17 MIN
SERVES 4

1 Spray a large nonstick skillet with nonstick spray and set over medium heat. Add the shrimp and cook, stirring occasionally, until just opaque in the center, about 5 minutes. Transfer the shrimp to a plate. When cool enough to handle, peel and devein the shrimp. Set aside.

2 Spray the same skillet with nonstick spray (no need to clean it) and set over medium heat. Add the onion and garlic; cook, stirring occasionally, until softened, about 5 minutes.

3 Add all the remaining ingredients except the bass to the skillet. Increase the heat to medium-high and cook, stirring occasionally, until the wine is reduced by half, about 3 minutes. Place the bass fillets in the skillet in a single layer. Reduce the heat and simmer, covered, about 2 minutes. Turn the fillets and top with the shrimp. Cook, covered, just until the shrimp are heated through and the fish is opaque in the center, 2–3 minutes.

PER SERVING (½ fillet, ¼ of sauce, and about 6 shrimp): 159 Cal, 2 g Fat, 0 g Sat Fat, 0 g Trans Fat, 113 mg Chol, 306 mg Sod, 6 g Carb, 1 g Fib, 28 g Prot, 43 mg Calc. **POINTS** value: **3.**

☼ MAKE IT CORE Substitute ½ cup clam juice for the wine and, because clam juice is quite salty, omit the salt.

Shrimp Seviche with Popcorn

1 pound small shrimp, peeled and deveined

1 small red onion, thinly sliced

6 tablespoons fresh lemon juice

6 tablespoons fresh lime juice

1 jalapeño chile pepper, seeded and finely chopped (wear gloves to prevent irritation)

¼ cup packed fresh cilantro leaves

2 teaspoons olive oil

¼ teaspoon salt

2 tomatoes, seeded and chopped

4 Bibb lettuce leaves

1 cup plain air-popped popcorn

HANDS-ON PREP 20 MIN
COOK NONE
SERVES 4

1 Combine the shrimp, onion, lemon and lime juice, jalapeño pepper, cilantro, oil, and salt in a large bowl. Refrigerate, tightly covered, until the shrimp are just opaque in the center, at least 4 hours or up to 24 hours.

2 Stir the tomatoes into the shrimp mixture. Divide the lettuce evenly among 4 plates. Using a slotted spoon, top with 1 cup of the seviche and sprinkle with ¼ cup of the popcorn. Serve at once.

PER SERVING (1 plate): 112 Cal, 3 g Fat, 1 g Sat Fat, 0 g Trans Fat, 107 mg Chol, 284 mg Sod, 9 g Carb, 2 g Fib, 13 g Prot, 40 mg Calc. *POINTS* value: *2.*

✸ GOOD IDEA **Round out this Ecuadorian dish with some traditional sides, such as black olives and sliced hard-cooked egg (10 small brine-cured olives and ½ large egg will increase the per-serving *POINTS* value by 2).**

Mexicali Shrimp in Pumpkin Seed Sauce

2 pounds large shrimp, unpeeled
½ cup shelled pumpkin seeds
3 tomatoes, chopped
2 yellow bell peppers, seeded and chopped
2 onions, finely chopped
2 jalapeño chile peppers, seeded and chopped (wear gloves to prevent irritation)
3 tablespoons chopped fresh cilantro
1 garlic clove, chopped
¼ teaspoon salt
1 tablespoon canola oil

HANDS-ON PREP 25 MIN
COOK 25 MIN
SERVES 6

1 Fill a large pot halfway with water and bring to a boil. Add the shrimp and cook until just opaque in the center, 2–3 minutes. Using a slotted spoon, transfer the shrimp to a medium bowl; reserve the shrimp cooking liquid. When cool enough to handle, peel and devein the shrimp. Set aside the shells and shrimp.

2 Add the shrimp shells to the cooking liquid and return to a boil. Boil about 5 minutes. Strain the cooking liquid through a sieve set over a bowl; discard the shells. Set the cooking liquid aside.

3 Pulse the pumpkin seeds in a food processor until finely ground; transfer to a small bowl. Put all the remaining ingredients except the oil in the food processor and puree. Return the pumpkin seeds to the food processor and pulse until blended.

4 Heat the oil in a large nonstick skillet over medium heat. Add the pumpkin seed mixture and cook, stirring occasionally, until heated through, about 5 minutes. Gradually stir in about 1 cup of the reserved shrimp cooking liquid, about 2 tablespoons at a time, until the sauce is the consistency of heavy cream. Discard the remaining cooking liquid. Add the shrimp to the sauce and cook, stirring occasionally, until heated through, about 5 minutes.

PER SERVING (8 shrimp and about ½ cup sauce): 234 Cal, 11 g Fat, 2 g Sat Fat, 0 g Trans Fat, 142 mg Chol, 282 mg Sod, 12 g Carb, 3 g Fib, 24 g Prot, 58 mg Calc. **POINTS** value: **5.**

5 MUST-HAVE INGREDIENTS

Here are some of the most common, and delicious, Hispanic ingredients. Look for them in the ethnic food aisle in supermarkets, in local Hispanic markets, in specialty food stores, and online.

ACHIOTE SEEDS Very hard, rust red seeds, used in seasoning pastes to add color. Grind them in a spice grinder or electric coffee mill.

JICAMA A slightly nutty tasting tuber that is available in supermarkets and can be eaten cooked or raw. Its creamy colored flesh resembles water chestnuts in both flavor and texture. Peel it, cut into strips, and add to salads and salsas.

MASA HARINA Parched corn that is treated with lime and then ground. It can be found in most supermarkets in the ethnic food aisle and in Hispanic markets. Masa harina is a necessary component for authentic corn tortillas.

PLANTAIN This relative of the banana is wonderfully versatile. When pale green, it is starchy and can be used like potatoes in soups and stews. When ripe-yellow, it can be cooked, then mashed, grilled, or sautéed for a side dish. When black-ripe, it can be baked like a sweet potato. Use a knife to cut it into thirds, then cut along the ridges of the skin and remove the peel.

QUESO FRESCO Also known as queso blanco, it is a white, slightly salty, fresh Mexican cheese with a texture similar to farmer cheese.

YUCATÁN-STYLE SHRIMP

Yucatán-Style Shrimp

2 pounds medium shrimp, unpeeled
2 large plum tomatoes, chopped
1 small red onion, finely chopped
2 tablespoons fresh lime juice
2 tablespoon chopped fresh cilantro
1 tablespoon extra-virgin olive oil
½ teaspoon ground cumin
¼ teaspoon salt
¼ teaspoon freshly ground pepper
4 romaine lettuce leaves
4 radishes, thinly sliced
Lime slices

HANDS-ON PREP 20 MIN
COOK 17 MIN
SERVES 4

1 Fill a large pot halfway with water and bring to a boil. Add the shrimp and cook until just opaque in the center, about 2 minutes; drain in a colander. Rinse the shrimp under cold running water; drain.

2 Peel and devein the shrimp; transfer to a large bowl. Stir in the tomatoes, onion, lime juice, cilantro, oil, cumin, salt, and pepper. Cover and refrigerate at least 2 hours or up to 6 hours.

3 Place a romaine lettuce leaf on each of 4 plates. Top with one-fourth of the shrimp mixture and the radishes. Serve with lime slices.

PER SERVING (1 plate): 165 Cal, 5 g Fat, 1 g Sat Fat, 0 g Trans Fat, 213 mg Chol, 401 mg Sod, 7 g Carb, 2 g Fib, 24 g Prot, 68 mg Calc. *POINTS* value: *3.*

☀ FOOD NOTE Feel free to make this dish hotter by adding a seeded and finely chopped jalapeño chile pepper or a generous pinch of cayenne to the marinade in step 2.

Cantina Shrimp with Lime-Drenched Onions

2 onions, thinly sliced

2 tablespoons fresh lime juice

1 tablespoon olive oil

1 pound large shrimp, unpeeled

2 tablespoons white-wine vinegar

¼ teaspoon salt

Pinch freshly ground pepper

HANDS-ON PREP 15 MIN
COOK 8 MIN
SERVES 4

1 Combine half of the onions and the lime juice in a medium nonreactive bowl. Let stand at room temperature until the flavors are blended, at least 30 minutes or up to 2 hours.

2 Heat the oil in a large nonstick skillet over medium heat. Add the remaining half of the onions and cook, stirring occasionally, until softened, about 5 minutes. Add the shrimp, vinegar, salt, and pepper. Increase the heat and cook, stirring constantly, until the shrimp are just opaque in the center and the vinegar is evaporated, about 3 minutes. Transfer the shrimp mixture to a platter and let cool about 15 minutes. Serve the shrimp topped with the marinated onions.

PER SERVING (6 shrimp and about ⅓ cup onions): 110 Cal, 4 g Fat, 1 g Sat Fat, 0 g Trans Fat, 107 mg Chol, 273 mg Sod, 7 g Carb, 1 g Fib, 12 g Prot, 35 mg Calc. *POINTS* value: *2.*

☀ GOOD IDEA **For even fresher flavor, add some cilantro leaves and/or a pinch of ground coriander to the marinated onions in Step 1.**

Shrimp, Spinach, and Scallion Omelette

1 tablespoon canola oil

1 red bell pepper, seeded and chopped

6 scallions, chopped

1 jalapeño chile pepper, seeded and minced (wear gloves to prevent irritation)

3 cups packed baby spinach leaves

¼ teaspoon salt

¼ teaspoon freshly ground pepper

¾ pound cooked small shrimp

8 egg whites

4 large eggs

HANDS-ON PREP 15 MIN
COOK 20 MIN
SERVES 6

1 Heat the oil in a large heavy nonstick skillet over medium heat. Add the bell pepper, scallions, and jalapeño pepper; cook, stirring occasionally, until softened, about 5 minutes. Add the spinach, salt, and ground pepper; cook, stirring frequently, until the spinach wilts, about 5 minutes. Stir in the shrimp.

2 Meanwhile, whisk together the egg whites and eggs in a large bowl. Pour the eggs into the shrimp mixture in the skillet. Cook, gently moving the eggs from the edge of the skillet towards the center, allowing the uncooked eggs to flow underneath, about 5 minutes. Cover and cook until the top is set, 6–8 minutes.

3 Remove the skillet from the heat. Let the omelette stand, covered, until firm and set, about 5 minutes. Cut into 6 wedges.

PER SERVING (1 wedge): 165 Cal, 7 g Fat, 1 g Sat Fat, 0 g Trans Fat, 252 mg Chol, 355 mg Sod, 4 g Carb, 1 g Fib, 22 g Prot, 70 mg Calc. **POINTS** value: **4.**

☼ EXPRESS LANE **Save time in the kitchen by using frozen cooked shrimp, available in the supermarket in bags and often in bulk—a really good buy. For speed and an even skinnier omelette, substitute 2 cups fat-free egg substitute for the eggs and egg whites in this recipe.**

Mexican Beer–Steamed Mussels

1 large tomato, chopped

¼ cup finely chopped onion

¼ cup chopped fresh cilantro

2 serrano chile peppers, seeded and finely chopped (wear gloves to prevent irritation)

1 garlic clove, minced

1 teaspoon fresh lime juice

⅛ teaspoon salt

1 (12-ounce) bottle light Mexican beer

1 pint cherry or grape tomatoes, halved

4 scallions, thinly sliced

2 pounds mussels, scrubbed and debearded

HANDS-ON PREP 20 MIN
COOK 15 MIN
SERVES 4

1 To make the salsa, combine the tomato, onion, cilantro, serrano peppers, garlic, lime juice, and salt in a small bowl; set aside.

2 Combine the beer, half of the cherry tomatoes, and half of the scallions in a Dutch oven. Cover and bring to a boil over medium-high heat. Reduce the heat and simmer about 5 minutes. Add the mussels and simmer, covered, until they open, about 5 minutes. Discard any mussels that do not open.

3 Stir the remaining half of the cherry tomatoes and scallions and ½ cup of the salsa into the Dutch oven. Spoon the mussels and sauce into 4 large shallow bowls and serve the remaining salsa on the side.

PER SERVING (16 mussels, about ⅓ cup sauce, and 2 tablespoons salsa): 127 Cal, 1 g Fat, 0 g Sat Fat, 0 g Trans Fat, 34 mg Chol, 141 mg Sod, 12 g Carb, 2 g Fib, 15 g Prot, 81 mg Calc. *POINTS* value: *2.*

☀ PLAY IT SAFE **When purchasing mussels, look for tightly closed shells or shells that close when lightly tapped. Discard any mussels whose shells remain open.**

MEXICAN BEER–STEAMED
MUSSELS

Crab-Filled Soft Corn Tacos

2 teaspoons canola oil

1 small onion, finely
chopped

1 garlic clove, minced

½ teaspoon ground
coriander

⅛ teaspoon ground allspice

2 plum tomatoes, chopped

3 cups finely shredded
green cabbage

¼ teaspoon salt

¼ teaspoon freshly ground
pepper

¼ cup chopped fresh
cilantro

2 tablespoons fresh lime
juice

½ pound fresh or thawed
frozen lump crabmeat,
picked over

8 (6-inch) corn tortillas,
warmed

Lime wedges

HANDS-ON PREP 20 MIN
COOK 15 MIN
SERVES 4

1 Heat the oil in a large nonstick skillet over medium heat. Add the onion and garlic; cook, stirring occasionally, until softened, about 5 minutes. Add the coriander and allspice; cook, stirring constantly, until fragrant, about 1 minute. Add the tomatoes and cook, stirring occasionally, until softened, about 3 minutes. Add the cabbage, salt, and pepper; cook, stirring occasionally, until softened, about 6 minutes. Stir in 2 tablespoons of the cilantro and 1 tablespoon of the lime juice. Remove the skillet from the heat.

2 Combine the crabmeat, the remaining 2 tablespoons cilantro and the remaining 1 tablespoon lime juice in a medium bowl.

3 Top each tortilla with about ¼ cup of the cabbage mixture and ¼ cup of the crab mixture. Fold each taco in half and serve at once with lime wedges.

PER SERVING (2 tacos): 212 Cal, 5 g Fat, 1 g Sat Fat, 0 g Trans Fat, 53 mg Chol, 386 mg Sod, 30 g Carb, 5 g Fib, 15 g Prot, 178 mg Calc. **POINTS** value: **4.**

☼ HOW WE DID IT **Because we use just a trace amount of oil in the filling, the cabbage might stick a bit to the skillet in Step 1. If that happens, add a little water to the pan and continue cooking the cabbage until softened.**

Brazilian Shellfish with Rice

SHRIMP STOCK

½ pound medium shrimp,
    unpeeled
1 tablespoon olive oil
5 cups water
2 scallions, sliced
2 fresh cilantro sprigs
8 whole black peppercorns
Pinch dried thyme
¼ teaspoon salt

SHELLFISH AND RICE

1 tablespoon olive oil
1 medium red onion,
    finely chopped
2 red jalapeño chile
    peppers, seeded and
    cut into thin strips
    (wear gloves to prevent
    irritation)
2 garlic cloves, chopped
2 cups long-grain white rice
½ pound sea scallops,
    halved if large
12 littleneck or cherrystone
    clams, scrubbed
4 tablespoons chopped
    fresh cilantro
12 raw oysters, shucked,
    juices drained

HANDS-ON PREP 30 MIN
COOK 1 HR 15 MIN
SERVES 6

1 To make the shrimp stock, peel and devein the shrimp; reserve the shells. Place the shrimp in a medium bowl; cover and set aside in the refrigerator.

2 Heat the oil in a Dutch oven over medium heat. Add the shrimp shells and cook, stirring occasionally, until bright pink, about 2 minutes. Add the water, scallions, cilantro sprigs, peppercorns, and thyme; increase the heat and bring to a boil. Reduce the heat and simmer, covered, until the flavors are blended, about 30 minutes. Strain the stock through a sieve set over a large bowl; discard the solids. Stir in the salt. Set aside.

3 To make the shellfish and rice, heat the oil in the same Dutch oven over medium heat. Add the onion, jalapeño peppers, and garlic; cook, stirring occasionally, until softened, about 5 minutes. Stir in the rice until well coated. Add the shrimp stock and bring to a boil. Reduce the heat and cook, covered, until the rice is tender and stock is absorbed, about 20 minutes.

4 Stir in the reserved shrimp, the scallops, clams, and 2 tablespoons of the chopped cilantro. Cook, covered, until the clams open and the shrimp and scallops are just opaque in the center, 3–5 minutes. Discard any clams that do not open. Stir in the oysters and cook, covered, until their edges begin to curl, about 2 minutes. Serve, sprinkled with the remaining 2 tablespoons cilantro.

PER SERVING (1⅔ cups): 393 Cal, 7 g Fat, 1 g Sat Fat,
0 g Trans Fat, 78 mg Chol, 286 mg Sod, 58 g Carb, 1 g Fib,
22 g Prot, 96 mg Calc. **POINTS** value: **8**.

Meatless Tacos, Tamales, and More

CHAPTER 7

Tofu in Adobo

2 dried ancho chile
peppers, seeded (wear
gloves to prevent
irritation)
2 dried New Mexico red
chile peppers, seeded
(wear gloves to prevent
irritation)
3 cups water
¼ cup apple-cider vinegar
¼ cup ketchup
1 onion, thinly sliced
2 garlic cloves, sliced
1 teaspoon ground cumin
1 teaspoon dried oregano
1 teaspoon dried marjoram
1 (3-inch) cinnamon stick
2 (14-ounce) packages
extra-firm tofu, cut into
1-inch cubes
2 cups canned white
corn kernels, rinsed
and drained
2 cups frozen broccoli
florets, thawed
½ cup shredded fat-free
cheddar cheese

HANDS-ON PREP 15 MIN
COOK 55 MIN
SERVES 8

1 To make the adobo sauce, set a large saucepan over
medium heat until hot, about 30 seconds. Add the
ancho and New Mexico chiles, one at a time, and toast
just until very fragrant, about 20 seconds on each side.
Transfer the toasted chiles to a plate.

2 Add the water, vinegar, ketchup, chiles, onion, garlic,
cumin, oregano, marjoram, and cinnamon stick to the
saucepan; bring to a boil. Reduce the heat and simmer,
stirring occasionally, until the chiles soften, about
20 minutes. Remove the pan from the heat and let stand
about 10 minutes. Remove the cinnamon stick; discard.

3 Pour the chile mixture into a food processor and
process until smooth. Put the tofu in a large bowl and
pour the chile adobo sauce on top. Toss gently; cover
and refrigerate at least 6 hours or up to overnight.

4 Preheat the oven to 350°F. Add the corn and broccoli
to the tofu and toss to combine. Transfer to a 9 x 13-
inch baking dish; bake about 15 minutes. Sprinkle the
cheese on top and bake until heated through and the
cheese melts and browns slightly, about 15 minutes.

PER SERVING (1½ cups): 190 Cal, 8 g Fat, 1 g Sat Fat,
0 g Trans Fat, 1 mg Chol, 283 mg Sod, 19 g Carb, 3 g Fib,
16 g Prot, 206 mg Calc. **POINTS** value: **4.**

GOOD IDEA **Adobo is a traditional Mexican
sauce made from dried chile peppers and aromatic
herbs; the mixture varies from cook to cook.**

"Unfried" Tofu Tostadas

2 garlic cloves, crushed through a press
2 tablespoons chili powder
2 tablespoons fresh lime juice
1 (14-ounce) package extra-firm tofu, cut crosswise into 8 slices
1 red bell pepper, seeded and thinly sliced
1 green bell pepper, seeded and thinly sliced
1 onion, sliced
8 (6-inch) fat-free corn tortillas, warmed
2 cups shredded romaine lettuce
1 large tomato, diced

HANDS-ON PREP 20 MIN
COOK 12 MIN
SERVES 4

1 Combine the garlic, chili powder, and lime juice in a small bowl and mix until a paste forms. Spread the paste over the tofu slices and place in a medium bowl. Cover and refrigerate, gently turning once or twice, at least 12 hours or up to 24 hours.

2 Spray a large nonstick skillet with nonstick spray and set over medium heat. Add the bell peppers and onion; cook, stirring, until softened, about 4 minutes. Transfer to a medium bowl.

3 Spray the same skillet (no need to clean it) with nonstick spray and set over medium heat. Place the tofu in the skillet in a single layer and add any remaining marinade. Cook, turning once, until the tofu is lightly browned, 1–3 minutes on each side.

4 Place 2 tortillas on each of 4 plates. Top each with 1 tofu slice, one-fourth of the bell pepper mixture, ¼ cup lettuce, and about 3 tablespoons tomato.

PER SERVING (2 tostadas): 267 Cal, 9 g Fat, 1 g Sat Fat, 0 g Trans Fat, 0 mg Chol, 135 mg Sod, 36 g Carb, 7 g Fib, 17 g Prot, 236 mg Calc. **POINTS** value: **5.**

☼ TRY IT **Tostadas are standard fare on most Tex-Mex restaurant menus, but they are usually fried and rarely filled with tofu—and that's a shame because creamy tofu makes them both heart-healthy and satisfying.**

Tempeh Salpicón

1 garlic clove, minced
5 tablespoons fresh lime
  juice
1 tablespoon chili powder
½ teaspoon ground cumin
½ teaspoon salt
1 pound tempeh
1 pound small potatoes,
  preferably purple
½ cup frozen corn kernels,
  thawed
6 radishes, thinly sliced
2 scallions, thinly sliced
3 cups shredded romaine
  lettuce
⅓ cup chopped fresh
  cilantro
4 dashes hot pepper
  sauce, or to taste

HANDS-ON PREP 20 MIN
COOK 40 MIN
SERVES 4

1 Mix together the garlic, 1 tablespoon of the lime juice, the chili powder, cumin, and salt in a small bowl until a paste forms. Rub the paste all over the tempeh and put into the bowl. Cover and refrigerate at least 6 hours or up to overnight.

2 Meanwhile, bring a large saucepan of water to a boil. Add the potatoes and cook until tender when pierced with a knife, about 20 minutes. Drain in a colander and cool briefly under cold running water. Cut the potatoes into quarters; set aside.

3 Spray the grill rack with nonstick spray; prepare the grill. Place the tempeh on the grill rack and grill until lightly browned, about 2 minutes on each side. Cut the tempeh into thin strips.

4 Toss the potatoes, tempeh, corn, radishes, scallions, lettuce, and cilantro in a serving bowl. Sprinkle with the remaining 4 tablespoons lime juice and the hot pepper sauce; toss to coat.

PER SERVING (1½ cups): 343 Cal, 13 g Fat, 3 g Sat Fat, 0 g Trans Fat, 0 mg Chol, 344 mg Sod, 39 g Carb, 9 g Fib, 24 g Prot, 183 mg Calc. *POINTS* value: *7.*

✹ FOOD NOTE *Salpicón*, **a dish consisting of purple potato salad and grilled steak, is considered by many South Americans to be the national dish of Chile. In our richly flavored version, tempeh stands in for the steak.**

Hot-and-Sweet Pepper Soft Tacos

1 jalapeño chile pepper

1 onion, cut into ½-inch-thick rounds

4 cups boiling water

½ cup apple-cider vinegar

½ cup cold water

2 teaspoons sugar

1 green bell pepper, seeded and chopped

2 garlic cloves, minced

1 (14-ounce) package textured soy protein

1 teaspoon chili powder

1 teaspoon ground cumin

1 teaspoon dried oregano

½ teaspoon onion powder

½ teaspoon paprika

¼ teaspoon freshly ground pepper

¼ cup canned tomato sauce

4 (8-inch) fat-free whole-wheat flour tortillas, warmed

HANDS-ON PREP 20 MIN
COOK 10 MIN
SERVES 4

1 Use a small sharp knife to cut a lengthwise slit in the jalapeño pepper; set aside. Separate the onion slices into rings and put into a colander in the sink. Pour the boiling water over the onion; drain. Transfer the onion to a large nonreactive bowl. Stir in the vinegar, cold water, and sugar; tuck the jalapeño into the onion. Cover and refrigerate until the onion is pickled, at least overnight or up to 4 days. (The longer the onion sits, the more pickled it will be.) Drain the onion; discard the jalapeño.

2 Spray a large nonstick skillet with nonstick spray and set over medium heat. Add the bell pepper and cook, stirring, until softened, about 2 minutes. Add the garlic and cook about 20 seconds. Add the textured soy protein, chili powder, cumin, oregano, onion powder, paprika, and ground pepper; cook, stirring, about 1 minute. Add the tomato sauce and reduce the heat to low. Cook, stirring constantly, until thickened, about 5 minutes.

3 Place one-fourth of the bell pepper mixture on each tortilla and fold the taco in half. Top each taco with one-fourth of the pickled onion and serve at once.

PER SERVING (1 taco): 277 Cal, 2 g Fat, 0 g Sat Fat, 0 g Trans Fat, 0 mg Chol, 311 mg Sod, 34 g Carb, 7 g Fib, 34 g Prot, 127 mg Calc. **POINTS** value: **5.**

TRY IT **Textured soy protein, also known as TSP, is found in the refrigerated case in supermarkets and health-food stores.**

GRILLED TEMPEH WITH
TOMATO-MINT SALSA

Grilled Tempeh with Tomato-Mint Salsa

1 orange, peeled and
finely chopped

2 tablespoons red-wine
or sherry vinegar

4 teaspoons
Worcestershire sauce

2 teaspoons Dijon mustard

2 teaspoons drained
capers, rinsed and
chopped

1 pound tempeh, cut into
8 slices

6 plum tomatoes, chopped

1 scallion, thinly sliced

1 jalapeño chile pepper,
seeded and chopped
(wear gloves to prevent
irritation)

2 tablespoons chopped
fresh mint

1 tablespoon fresh lime
juice

½ teaspoon salt

¼ teaspoon freshly ground
pepper

Lime slices

HANDS-ON PREP 15 MIN
COOK 4 MIN
SERVES 4

1 Combine the orange, vinegar, Worcestershire sauce, mustard, and capers in a shallow baking dish. Add the tempeh and turn to coat well. Cover and refrigerate, turning a few times, at least 6 hours or up to overnight.

2 To make the salsa, combine all the remaining ingredients except the lime slices in a small bowl.

3 Spray the grill rack with nonstick spray; prepare the grill. Remove the tempeh from the marinade; discard the marinade. Grill the tempeh until lightly browned, about 2 minutes on each side. Serve with the tomato-mint salsa and lime slices.

PER SERVING (2 tempeh slices and ½ cup salsa): 243 Cal, 13 g Fat, 3 g Sat Fat, 0 g Trans Fat, 0 mg Chol, 350 mg Sod, 16 g Carb, 5 g Fib, 22 g Prot, 145 mg Calc. *POINTS* value: *5.*

✺ **TRY IT Tempeh, made from pressed soybeans, resembles tofu but is chewier and has a yeasty, nutty flavor. It's highly prized in Asian vegetarian cooking and is perfect in this South American–inspired dish. Round out the meal by serving with brown rice and romaine lettuce leaves (½ cup cooked brown rice per serving will increase the *POINTS* value by *2*, while romaine lettuce will add no *POINTS* value).**

Vegetarian Meatloaf

1 (14-ounce) package
textured soy protein
1 (4½-ounce) can chopped
mild, medium, or hot
green chiles, drained
2 tablespoons fresh whole-
wheat bread crumbs
2 tablespoons chopped
fresh cilantro
½ teaspoon onion powder
¼ teaspoon ground cumin
¼ teaspoon garlic powder
1 (8-ounce) jar taco sauce

HANDS-ON PREP 12 MIN
COOK 45 MIN
SERVES 4

1 Preheat the oven to 350°F. Spray a 9-inch square
nonstick baking pan with nonstick spray.

2 Combine all the ingredients except the taco sauce in
a large bowl. Shape into an 8-inch-long loaf. Place the
meatloaf in the baking dish and pour the taco sauce
over. Cover the dish with foil and bake until the meatloaf
is heated through and the sauce is bubbling, about
45 minutes. Cut into 8 slices and serve with the sauce.

PER SERVING (2 slices and about ¼ cup sauce): 173 Cal,
1 g Fat, 0 g Sat Fat, 0 g Trans Fat, 0 mg Chol, 362 mg Sod,
7 g Carb, 2 g Fib, 33 g Prot, 86 mg Calc. **POINTS** value: **3.**

✱ GOOD IDEA **Our flavorful meatloaf makes
delicious sandwiches for brown bagging. Place
2 slices of meatloaf between 2 slices of whole-wheat
bread and top with some crisp lettuce leaves and
sliced tomato (the per-serving POINTS value will
increase by 2).**

Red Beans and Rice

1 (28-ounce) can diced
  tomatoes
1 small onion, chopped
1 green bell pepper, seeded
  and chopped
2 teaspoons dried thyme
1 teaspoon dried marjoram
½ teaspoon cayenne
1 (15-ounce) can red kidney
  beans, rinsed and drained
2 cups cooked brown rice
¼ cup chopped fresh
  cilantro
2 teaspoons sherry vinegar

HANDS-ON PREP 5 MIN
COOK 40 MIN
SERVES 4

1 Combine the tomatoes, onion, bell pepper, thyme, marjoram, and cayenne in a large saucepan; bring to a boil. Reduce the heat and simmer, covered, about 5 minutes. Add the beans and simmer, covered, about 15 minutes.

2 Stir the rice and cilantro into the tomato mixture. Simmer, stirring often, until most of the liquid is absorbed, about 10 minutes. Stir in the vinegar and remove the saucepan from the heat. Let stand, covered, about 5 minutes before serving.

PER SERVING (1½ cups): 248 Cal, 2 g Fat, 0 g Sat Fat, 0 g Trans Fat, 0 mg Chol, 691 mg Sod, 50 g Carb, 11 g Fib, 11 g Prot, 112 mg Calc. *POINTS* value: **4.**

☀ GOOD IDEA **Turn this dish into a complete meal by serving a vinegar-dressed salad of celery, cucumbers, and tomato alongside.**

Black Bean and Swiss Chard Burritos

1 onion, chopped
1 garlic clove, minced
1 (15-ounce) can black beans, rinsed and drained
1 bunch Swiss chard, stemmed, leaves chopped (about 6 packed cups)
¼ cup prepared chipotle chile salsa
2 tablespoons water
2 teaspoons ground cumin
1 teaspoon dried oregano
¼ teaspoon freshly ground pepper
¼ teaspoon salt
4 (8-inch) fat-free whole-wheat flour tortillas
4 tablespoons shredded reduced-fat pepperjack cheese

HANDS-ON PREP: 20 MIN
COOK: 15 MIN
SERVES: 4

1 Spray a large nonstick skillet with nonstick spray and set over medium heat. Add the onion and cook, stirring, until softened, about 5 minutes. Add the garlic and cook about 20 seconds. Stir in all the remaining ingredients except the tortillas and cheese. Cook, covered, until the chard wilts and is tender, about 7 minutes. Uncover and cook until all the liquid evaporates, about 2 minutes.

2 Remove the skillet from the heat and let stand about 5 minutes. Place one-fourth of the greens mixture along the center of each tortilla and sprinkle each with 1 tablespoon cheese. Fold two opposite sides of each tortilla over to enclose the filling.

PER SERVING (1 burrito): 273 Cal, 3 g Fat, 1 g Sat Fat, 0 g Trans Fat, 5 mg Chol, 885 mg Sod, 51 g Carb, 11 g Fib, 14 g Prot, 206 mg Calc. **POINTS** value: **5.**

✹ EXPRESS LANE **You can make the burrito filling up to 2 days ahead and store in an airtight container in the refrigerator. To warm the filling, microwave on High until heated through, about 3 minutes. Serve with your favorite fresh tomato salsa, if you like.**

**BLACK BEAN AND SWISS
CHARD BURRITOS**

Colombian Pinto Bean Casserole

2 (15-ounce) cans pinto
beans, rinsed and
drained
1 (14-ounce) can reduced-
sodium diced tomatoes
1 (14½-ounce) can reduced-
sodium vegetable broth
¼ cup brewed espresso or
very strong coffee
¼ cup apple-cider vinegar
1 onion, chopped
3 tablespoons dark brown
sugar
1 teaspoon dried thyme
1 teaspoon dry mustard
½ teaspoon salt
½ teaspoon crushed red
pepper
1 bay leaf
¼ cup shredded low-fat
Monterey Jack cheese

HANDS-ON PREP 10 MIN
COOK 2 HOURS
SERVES 4

1 Preheat the oven to 350°F.

2 Combine the beans, tomatoes, broth, espresso,
vinegar, onion, brown sugar, thyme, dry mustard, salt,
crushed red pepper, and bay leaf in a large Dutch oven
or casserole dish. Cover and bake until the liquid is
reduced to a thick sauce, about 2 hours. (If the sauce
gets too thick, add some water, ½ cup at a time.) To
serve, spoon the bean mixture into 4 shallow bowls and
top with the cheese.

PER SERVING (about 1½ cups bean mixture and 1 tablespoon
cheese): 304 Cal, 3 g Fat, 1 g Sat Fat, 0 g Trans Fat, 5 mg Chol,
717 mg Sod, 56 g Carb, 14 g Fib, 16 g Prot, 165 mg Calc.
POINTS value: **6.**

☀ GOOD IDEA **This is guaranteed to be a
recipe you will turn to often. The recipe doubles
easily and can be made up to 2 days ahead. Reheat
it slowly in a saucepan, adding a bit more liquid if
needed to keep it saucy.**

Chilean Quiche

3 sheets thawed frozen
   phyllo dough, cut
   crosswise in half
¼ cup shredded fat-free
   cheddar cheese
4 large eggs
1 cup fat-free milk
1 (10-ounce) package
   frozen chopped spinach,
   thawed and squeezed dry
¼ cup canned black beans,
   rinsed and drained
2 tablespoons chopped
   pitted green olives

HANDS-ON PREP 20 MIN
COOK 45 MIN
SERVES 6

1 Preheat the oven to 350°F. Spray a 9-inch pie plate with nonstick spray.

2 Cover the phyllo with plastic wrap and a damp towel to prevent the sheets from drying out. Place 1 phyllo sheet in the pie plate to form a "shell"; lightly spray with nonstick spray. Place a second sheet on top with the corners at different angles from the first sheet; spray with nonstick spray. Repeat with the remaining phyllo but do not spray. Sprinkle the cheese evenly over the bottom of the phyllo shell.

3 Beat together the eggs and milk in a large bowl. Stir in the spinach, black beans, and olives. Pour into the shell. Bake until a knife inserted into the center comes out clean, about 45 minutes. Cut into 6 wedges and serve at once.

PER SERVING (⅙ of quiche): 138 Cal, 4 g Fat, 1 g Sat Fat, 0 g Trans Fat, 143 mg Chol, 259 mg Sod, 15 g Carb, 2 g Fib, 10 g Prot, 164 mg Calc. **POINTS** value: **3.**

☀ ZAP IT **Quiche makes tasty leftovers, but it needs to be warmed up. Put one wedge on a plate and microwave on Medium power until heated through, about 3 minutes. Serve with a lettuce and tomato salad with a squeeze of fresh lime juice.**

HUEVOS MEXICANOS

Huevos Mexicanos

4 plum tomatoes,
quartered
1 small onion, quartered
1 pickled jalapeño pepper,
seeded
2 tablespoons fresh
cilantro leaves
¼ teaspoon salt
½ teaspoon distilled
white vinegar
4 large eggs
4 tablespoons shredded
fat-free pepperjack
cheese
4 (6-inch) fat-free corn
tortillas, warmed

HANDS-ON PREP 10 MIN
COOK 8 MIN
SERVES 4

1 To make the salsa, put the tomatoes, onion, pickled jalapeño, cilantro, and salt in a food processor and pulse until coarsely chopped. Transfer to a small bowl and set aside.

2 Fill a large skillet halfway with water and bring to a boil over high heat. Add the vinegar and reduce the heat so the water simmers slowly. Slip in the eggs, one at a time, waiting about 10 seconds before adding another egg. Poach just until set, about 1 minute. Using a slotted spoon, transfer the eggs to a paper towel–lined plate to drain.

3 Place 1 tortilla on each of 4 plates and top with an egg. Sprinkle each with 1 tablespoon cheese and top with one-fourth of the salsa. Serve at once.

PER SERVING (1 filled tortilla): 163 Cal, 6 g Fat, 2 g Sat Fat, 0 g Trans Fat, 213 mg Chol, 428 mg Sod, 17 g Carb, 2 g Fib, 10 g Prot, 140 mg Calc. *POINTS* value: *3.*

☀ HOW WE DID IT **The best way to add eggs to a pot of boiling water is to crack one into a ramekin or onto a small plate, then gently slip it into the water; repeat with the remaining eggs. To fit this recipe into the Core Plan, substitute cooked thinly sliced potatoes for the corn tortillas.**

Venezuelan-Style Stuffed Eggplant

3 small eggplants (about ¾ pound each)
1 onion, chopped
2 garlic cloves, minced
1 tomato, chopped
½ pound fresh cremini or white mushrooms, sliced
¾ pound green beans, trimmed and sliced
1 cup canned chickpeas, rinsed, drained, and coarsely chopped
½ cup chopped pitted black olives
¼ cup chopped fresh cilantro
¼ cup chopped fresh parsley
1 teaspoon dried thyme
4 dashes hot pepper sauce, or to taste

HANDS-ON PREP 20 MIN
COOK 1 HR 25 MIN
SERVES 6

1 Slice the eggplants lengthwise in half. Use a grapefruit spoon to remove the flesh, leaving a ½-inch-thick wall. Chop the flesh. Set aside the flesh and eggplant shells.

2 Preheat the oven to 350°F. Spray a jelly-roll pan with nonstick spray.

3 Spray a large nonstick skillet with nonstick spray and set over medium heat. Add the onion and cook, stirring, until softened, about 3 minutes. Add the garlic and cook about 20 seconds. Add the eggplant flesh and tomato; cook, stirring often, until the eggplant softens, releases its liquid, and the liquid is reduced to a glaze, about 10 minutes. Add the mushrooms and cook until they release their liquid, about 2 minutes. Stir in the remaining ingredients.

4 Remove the skillet from the heat; cover and let stand about 5 minutes. Spoon the filling into the eggplant halves, mounding it in the center. Place the eggplant halves in the jelly-roll pan and bake until tender and heated through, about 40 minutes.

PER SERVING (1 stuffed eggplant half): 162 Cal, 3 g Fat, 0 g Sat Fat, 0 g Trans Fat, 0 mg Chol, 147 mg Sod, 33 g Carb, 9 g Fib, 6 g Prot, 68 mg Calc. *POINTS* value: *3.*

✷ EXPRESS LANE **You can make this dish up to 1 day ahead. Prepare the filling and eggplant shells as directed, then cover and refrigerate.**

Vegetarian Sausage and Mushroom Pilaf

1 onion, chopped
½ pound fresh white
  mushrooms, sliced
½ pound vegetarian
  sausage links, cut into
  ½-inch-thick slices
1½ teaspoons ground cumin
½ teaspoon cinnamon
½ teaspoon salt
¼ teaspoon freshly ground
  pepper
¼ teaspoon nutmeg
1 cup brown rice
2½ cups reduced-sodium
  vegetable broth

HANDS-ON PREP 10 MIN
COOK 1 HOUR
SERVES 4

1 Preheat the oven to 350°F.

2 Spray a large saucepan with nonstick spray and set over medium heat. Add the onion and cook, stirring, until softened, about 5 minutes. Add the mushrooms and cook, stirring often, until they release their liquid and the liquid reduces to a glaze, about 6 minutes. Stir in the sausage, cumin, cinnamon, salt, pepper, and nutmeg; cook, stirring constantly, about 1 minute. Stir in the rice and broth; bring to a simmer.

3 Transfer to a baking dish or casserole dish. Cover and bake until the rice is tender and the liquid is absorbed, about 45 minutes.

Per serving (1¼ cups): 284 Cal, 5 g Fat, 1 g Sat Fat, 0 g Trans Fat, 0 mg Chol, 902 mg Sod, 45 g Carb, 7 g Fib, 16 g Prot, 67 mg Calc. *POINTS* value: *5.*

✦ FOOD NOTE **Vegetarian sausage, available in bulk and in sausage links, is a tasty and healthful alternative to high-fat pork sausage. Look for it in health-food stores and larger supermarkets.**

Fresh Mushroom Tamales

12 corn husks
2 tablespoons canola oil
1 (6-ounce) package fresh white mushrooms, sliced
1 cup masa harina
⅓ cup warm water, or more if needed
¼ cup chopped fresh cilantro
½ teaspoon baking powder
½ teaspoon cinnamon
¼ teaspoon salt
1½ cups prepared taco sauce, heated

HANDS-ON PREP 25 MIN
COOK 50 MIN
SERVES 4

1 Put the corn husks in a large bowl and add enough hot water to cover. Place a saucepan or skillet on top of the husks to keep them submerged. Set aside until softened, about 35 minutes.

2 Meanwhile, heat 1 tablespoon of the oil in a large nonstick skillet over medium heat. Add the mushrooms and cook until they release their liquid and it bubbles. Transfer to a large bowl; let stand about 5 minutes.

3 Add the masa harina, water, cilantro, the remaining 1 tablespoon oil, the baking powder, cinnamon, and salt to the mushrooms; stir until thick and pasty. If too thick, add warm water, 1 tablespoon at a time.

4 Drain the corn husks and pat dry with paper towels. Place the husks flat on a work surface. Spread a scant 2 tablespoons of the mushroom–masa dough mixure down the center of each husk, leaving a 1-inch border all around. Fold the two long sides over to enclose the filling, then fold the two short ends over.

5 Stand the tamales, side by side, in a large vegetable steamer. Place over a pot of simmering water and steam until the filling is firm, about 40 minutes. Remove the tamales from the steamer and cool about 5 minutes. Put 3 tamales on each of 4 plates, open them up, and spoon some taco sauce over each.

PER SERVING (3 tamales and 6 tablespoons taco sauce): 202 Cal, 8 g Fat, 1 g Sat Fat, 0 g Trans Fat, 0 mg Chol, 635 mg Sod, 30 g Carb, 5 g Fib, 5 g Prot, 110 mg Calc. **POINTS** value: **4.**

No-Fry Chile Rellenos

4 poblano chile peppers
1 onion, chopped
1 celery stalk, chopped
2 garlic cloves, minced
¾ cup cooked brown rice
½ cup frozen corn kernels, thawed
2 ounces soft goat cheese, crumbled
1½ cups prepared tomatillo salsa

HANDS-ON PREP 55 MIN
COOK 45 MIN
SERVES: 4

1 Line a baking sheet with foil and place the peppers on it. Preheat the broiler. Broil 5 inches from the heat, turning often with tongs, until blackened all over, about 10 minutes. Wrap the peppers in the foil and set aside about 10 minutes.

2 Preheat the oven to 350°F.

3 Peel the blackened skin off the poblano peppers. Use a sharp knife to make a long slit in one side of each pepper; remove the seeds and membranes, being careful not to tear the peppers.

4 Spray a large nonstick skillet with nonstick spray and set over medium heat. Add the onion and celery; cook, stirring, until softened, about 3 minutes. Add the garlic and cook about 20 seconds. Remove the skillet from the heat and stir in the brown rice, corn, goat cheese, and ½ cup of the salsa. Set aside, stirring once or twice, about 5 minutes.

5 Gently stuff one-fourth of the rice mixture into each poblano pepper, mounding the filling and taking care not to split the skin. Place the peppers in a 9-inch square baking dish or casserole; pour the remaining 1 cup salsa on top. Cover the dish tightly with foil and bake until heated through, about 20 minutes.

PER SERVING (1 chile relleno): 154 Cal, 4 g Fat, 2 g Sat Fat, 0 g Trans Fat, 7 mg Chol, 250 mg Sod, 25 g Carb, 5 g Fib, 6 g Prot, 52 mg Calc. *POINTS* value: *3.*

Spicy Bean, Tomato, and Cheese–Stuffed Zucchini

2 poblano chile peppers

4 large zucchini

1 onion, chopped

2 garlic cloves, minced

2 plum tomatoes, chopped

1 cup canned red kidney beans, rinsed and drained

¼ cup chopped fresh cilantro

1½ teaspoons dried oregano

½ teaspoon crushed red pepper

1 cup shredded Mexican-style four-cheese blend

HANDS-ON PREP 20 MIN
COOK 1 HR
SERVES 4

1 Char the peppers by holding them, one at a time, with tongs over an open gas flame, turning, until blackened, about 4 minutes. (Or preheat the broiler and broil 5 inches from the heat, turning, until blackened. Place the peppers in a zip-close plastic bag, seal, and set aside about 10 minutes.

2 Meanwhile, cut the zucchini lengthwise in half. Remove the flesh and chop it. Peel the blackened skin off the poblano peppers; seed and coarsely chop.

3 Preheat the oven to 350°F.

4 Spray a large nonstick skillet with nonstick spray and set over medium heat. Add the onion and cook, stirring, until softened, about 5 minutes. Add the garlic and cook about 20 seconds. Add the tomatoes and chopped zucchini flesh; cook, stirring, until softened, about 5 minutes. Add the beans, cilantro, oregano, and crushed red pepper; cook, stirring, until the beans have absorbed most of the liquid, about 2 minutes. Remove the skillet from the heat and stir in the cheese.

5 Place the zucchini shells in a 9 x 13-inch baking dish. Spoon one-fourth of the vegetable mixture into each shell, mounding it high. Bake until the filling is heated through about 25 minutes.

PER SERVING (2 stuffed zucchini halves): 250 Cal, 10 g Fat, 6 g Sat Fat, 0 g Trans Fat, 30 mg Chol, 318 mg Sod, 28 g Carb, 8 g Fib, 16 g Prot, 234 mg Calc. **POINTS** value: **5.**

SPICY BEAN, TOMATO, AND CHEESE-STUFFED ZUCCHINI

Caribbean-Seasoned Vegetable Casserole

2 large yellow plantains,
  peeled and thinly sliced
2 zucchini, thinly sliced
2 plum tomatoes,
  thinly sliced
1 carrot, thinly sliced
1 small onion, sliced
1 (8-ounce) package frozen
  artichoke hearts, thawed
¼ cup water
1 tablespoon sugar-free
  jerk seasoning mix

HANDS-ON PREP 10 MIN
COOK 1 HR
SERVES 4

1 Preheat the oven to 350°F.

2 Combine the plantains, zucchini, tomatoes, carrot, onion, artichoke hearts, water, and jerk seasoning in a Dutch oven or casserole dish. Cover and bake until the vegetables are tender and the juices are bubbling, about 1 hour.

PER SERVING (1½ cups): 247 Cal, 1 g Fat, 0 g Sat Fat, 0 g Trans Fat, 0 mg Chol, 91 mg Sod, 63 g Carb, 9 g Fib, 5 g Prot, 71 mg Calc. **POINTS** value: **4.**

⚜ FOOD NOTE Plantains, also known as "cooking bananas," are actually a large variety of the fruit. They are used extensively in Latin American cooking much like the potato, thanks to their firm flesh and squashlike taste. Look for plantains in most supermarkets in the produce aisle. The peel should be yellow and firm with a few brown spots, harder than a banana, but not at all green.

Roasted Vegetable Enchiladas

1 large acorn squash, peeled, seeded, and cubed

2 large parsnips, peeled and cut into ½-inch-thick slices

12 Brussels sprouts, thinly sliced lengthwise, then pulled into shreds

2 tablespoons chili powder

½ teaspoon cinnamon

¼ teaspoon salt

⅛ teaspoon cayenne

8 (8-inch) fat-free whole-wheat flour tortillas

4 tablespoons shredded low-fat Monterey Jack cheese

1 cup prepared enchilada sauce

HANDS-ON PREP 20 MIN
COOK 1 HR
SERVES 4

1 Preheat the oven to 400°F.

2 Place the squash and parsnips in a large baking dish; lightly spray with nonstick spray. Roast, stirring once or twice, until lightly browned and tender, about 40 minutes. Let cool about 5 minutes.

3 Reduce the oven temperature to 350°F. Add the Brussels sprouts, chili powder, cinnamon, salt, and cayenne to the squash and parsnips; toss to combine.

4 Lay the tortillas flat on a work surface and spoon one-fourth of the vegetable mixture on top. Sprinkle each with ½ tablespoon cheese, then roll each tortilla up, jelly-roll style. Place the enchiladas, seam side down, in a baking dish. Pour the enchilada sauce on top and bake until the sauce forms a glaze, about 20 minutes.

PER SERVING (2 enchiladas): 423 Cal, 5 g Fat, 2 g Sat Fat, 0 g Trans Fat, 5 mg Chol, 969 mg Sod, 88 g Carb, 20 g Fib, 17 g Prot, 270 mg Calc. **POINTS** value: **8.**

✸ FOOD NOTE Acorn squash is available year-round, but it is at its freshest in the fall and winter. When buying out of season, look for squash with firm, taut skin without any wrinkles or soft spots. The skin should be green with light orange to yellow coloring in places with no mottled brown areas.

Baked Tomato Rice with Vegetables

1 large onion, chopped

3 garlic cloves, minced

½ pound fresh cremini or white mushrooms, sliced

1 (28-ounce) can diced tomatoes

2 cups vegetable broth

1 (10-ounce) package frozen peas, thawed

2 cups broccoli florets

2 cups cauliflower florets

1½ cups brown rice

3 whole pimientos, drained and chopped

2 teaspoons dried oregano

½ teaspoon salt

½ teaspoon freshly ground pepper

¼ teaspoon saffron threads

¼ teaspoon nutmeg

2 bay leaves

HANDS-ON PREP 15 MIN

COOK 55 MIN

SERVES 8

1 Preheat the oven to 350°F.

2 Spray a large Dutch oven with nonstick spray and set over medium heat. Add the onion and cook, stirring, until softened, about 3 minutes. Add the garlic and cook about 20 seconds. Add the mushrooms and cook, stirring frequently, until their liquid is released and the liquid reduces to a glaze, about 6 minutes. Add the tomatoes and broth; cook, scraping up any browned bits in the bottom of the pan.

3 Stir the remaining ingredients into the mushroom mixture and bring to a boil. Cover and bake until the rice is tender and the liquid is almost absorbed, about 45 minutes. Discard the bay leaves and serve.

PER SERVING (1¼ cups): 209 Cal, 2 g Fat, 0 g Sat Fat, 0 g Trans Fat, 0 mg Chol, 571 mg Sod, 43 g Carb, 8 g Fib, 8 g Prot, 79 mg Calc. **POINTS** value: **4.**

✺ FOOD NOTE **Saffron is the most expensive spice in the world, so it is no wonder that it is often found safely stashed at the manager's desk at local markets. Its high cost is due to the fact that each small purple crocus flower contains only three stigmas, which must be hand-picked and then dried. The best-quality saffron is sold in long, delicate threads, often in highly decorated tin boxes.**

Sumptuous
Sides

CHAPTER 8

Mexican Black Beans

1 tablespoon olive oil

2 large garlic cloves, finely chopped

1 teaspoon ground cumin

2 (15½-ounce) cans black beans, rinsed and drained

1 (14½-ounce) can reduced-sodium chicken broth

1 teaspoon minced chipotles en adobo

¼ cup chopped fresh cilantro

2 teaspoons fresh lime juice

HANDS-ON PREP 10 MIN
COOK 20 MIN
SERVES 6

1 Heat the oil in a large saucepan over medium-high heat. Add the garlic and cumin; cook, stirring constantly, until fragrant, about 30 seconds. Stir in the beans, broth, and chipotle en adobo; bring to a boil.

2 Remove the bean mixture from the heat and coarsely mash with a potato masher. Cook, stirring occasionally, until slightly thickened, about 15 minutes. Just before serving, stir in the cilantro and lime juice.

PER SERVING (scant ½ cup): 170 Cal, 3 g Fat, 0 g Sat Fat, 0 g Trans Fat, 0 mg Chol, 557 mg Sod, 27 g Carb, 7 g Fib, 10 g Prot, 81 mg Calc. **POINTS** value: **3.**

✺ MAKE IT CORE These saucy black beans get their kick from chipotles en adobo—smoked jalapeño peppers in tomato sauce—but to make this recipe fit the **Core Plan**, you can substitute ½ teaspoon chipotle chile powder. These beans are a must with rice (½ cup cooked brown rice for each serving will increase the **POINTS** value by **2**).

Chickpeas with Chiles

2 teaspoons olive oil

1 onion, chopped

2 garlic cloves, finely
chopped

2 teaspoons ground cumin

1 teaspoon dried oregano

¼ teaspoon salt

¼ teaspoon freshly ground
pepper

2 (15½-ounce) cans
chickpeas, rinsed and
drained

⅓ cup canned diced green
chiles, drained

⅓ cup fat-free half-and-half

1 tablespoon fresh lime
juice

Chopped fresh cilantro
(optional)

Chopped scallions
(optional)

HANDS-ON PREP 15 MIN
COOK 10 MIN
SERVES 6

1 Heat the oil in a large nonstick skillet over medium heat. Add the onion and cook, stirring occasionally, until softened, about 5 minutes. Add the garlic, cumin, oregano, salt, and pepper; cook, stirring frequently, until fragrant, about 30 seconds.

2 Meanwhile, put the chickpeas in a food processor and pulse until finely chopped.

3 Stir the chickpeas into the onion mixture. Cook, occasionally stirring and mashing the chickpeas with the back of a spoon, until heated through and beginning to brown, about 3 minutes. Stir in the chiles, half-and-half, and lime juice. Just before serving, sprinkle with cilantro and scallions, if using.

PER SERVING (½ cup): 199 Cal, 4 g Fat, 1 g Sat Fat, 0 g Trans Fat, 1 mg Chol, 291 mg Sod, 32 g Carb, 7 g Fib, 10 g Prot, 80 mg Calc. *POINTS* value: *4.*

✸ FOOD NOTE Think of this as a healthful version of refried beans—one made with chickpeas. Canned chopped green chiles are quite mild and lend more of a tangy flavor than fiery finish to the dish. If the chickpeas seem a bit dry while heating them through, add a few tablespoons of water to the skillet.

Corn-and-Cheese Griddle Cakes

¾ **cup yellow cornmeal**
¼ **teaspoon salt**
½ **cup shredded fat-free mozzarella cheese**
4 **teaspoons butter, melted**
½ **cup low-fat (1%) milk**
⅔ **cup fresh or thawed frozen corn kernels**
Pico de Gallo (page 136), optional

HANDS-ON PREP 10 MIN
COOK 15 MIN
SERVES 6

1 Put the cornmeal and salt in a food processor and process until finely ground. Transfer to a large bowl and stir in the cheese and butter.

2 Meanwhile, heat the milk in a small saucepan over medium-high heat until almost boiling. Gradually stir enough of the milk into the cornmeal mixture to make a very thick batter. Stir in the corn.

3 Spray a large nonstick skillet with nonstick spray and set over medium heat. Drop half of the cornmeal mixture, 1 heaping tablespoon at a time, in mounds in the skillet. Flatten slightly and cook until golden brown, about 3 minutes. Spray the griddle cakes with nonstick spray and turn. Cook until golden, about 3 minutes, transferring them to a platter when they are done; keep warm. Repeat with the remaining cornmeal mixture to make a total of 12 griddle cakes. Serve with Pico de Gallo, if using.

PER SERVING (2 griddle cakes): 131 Cal, 4 g Fat, 2 g Sat Fat, 0 g Trans Fat, 9 mg Chol, 221 mg Sod, 19 g Carb, 1 g Fib, 5 g Prot, 110 mg Calc. *POINTS* value: *3*.

☼ GOOD IDEA These little griddle cakes, known as *arepas* in Spanish, are from Venezuela, where they are eaten at any time of the day, topped with cheese, meat, chicken, or eggs. We like ours served with roast pork or topped with a spoonful of pico de gallo as a delicious side or tempting appetizer.

Southwest-Style Corn and Hominy

2 poblano chile peppers
1 tablespoon canola oil
1 small red onion, chopped
2 garlic cloves, minced
1 teaspoon cumin seeds
  or ½ teaspoon ground
  cumin
½ teaspoon dried oregano
1 (15½-ounce) can white
  hominy, rinsed and
  drained
1 (10-ounce) package
  frozen corn kernels
¼ teaspoon salt
2 tablespoons chopped
  fresh cilantro
1 tablespoon fresh lime
  juice

HANDS-ON PREP 10 MIN
COOK 15 MIN
SERVES 4

1 Char the poblano peppers by holding them, one at a time, with tongs over an open gas flame, turning often, until blackened on all sides, about 5 minutes. (Or preheat the broiler and broil the peppers 5 inches from the heat, turning often, until blackened all over, about 10 minutes.) Place the peppers in a paper bag or heavy zip-close plastic bag and seal the bag. Set aside about 10 minutes. When the peppers are cool enough to handle, peel, discard the seeds, and coarsely chop.

2 Heat the oil in a large skillet over medium-high heat. Add the onion and cook, stirring occasionally, until softened, about 3 minutes. Add the garlic, cumin, and oregano; cook, stirring frequently, until fragrant, about 30 seconds. Add the hominy, corn, salt, and poblano peppers; cook, stirring occasionally, until heated through, about 4 minutes. Just before serving, stir in the cilantro and lime juice.

PER SERVING (1 cup): 165 Cal, 5 g Fat, 0 g Sat Fat, 0 g Trans Fat, 0 mg Chol, 324 mg Sod, 29 g Carb, 5 g Fib, 4 g Prot, 28 mg Calc. **POINTS** value: **3.**

TRY IT **Poblano chile peppers are available in many supermarkets, but if you have trouble finding them, substitute green bell peppers and add a dash of cayenne along with the spices in Step 2.**

Mashed Potatoes with Tomatillo Salsa

**2 pounds red potatoes,
 scrubbed and quartered**
**½ cup prepared fat-free
 tomatillo salsa**
⅓ cup fat-free sour cream
**2 tablespoons chopped
 fresh cilantro**
½ teaspoon salt

HANDS-ON PREP 12 MIN
COOK 25 MIN
SERVES 8

1 Bring the potatoes and enough water to cover to a boil in a large saucepan. Reduce the heat and simmer until the potatoes are tender, about 20 minutes. Drain the potatoes in a colander.

2 Return the potatoes to the saucepan and mash with a potato masher until smooth. Stir in the salsa, sour cream, cilantro, and salt and serve at once.

PER SERVING (½ cup): 98 Cal, 0 g Fat, 0 g Sat Fat, 0 g Trans Fat, 1 mg Chol, 484 mg Sod, 23 g Carb, 3 g Fib, 2 g Prot, 38 mg Calc. **POINTS** value: **1.**

✿ FOOD NOTE **Eaten with their skin, potatoes provide a good amount of vitamin C and are also an excellent source of potassium, fiber, and complex carbohydrates. Be sure to scrub them well to remove all the embedded dirt.**

SAUTÉED SUMMER SQUASH
WITH TOMATOES AND CORN

Sautéed Summer Squash with Tomatoes and Corn

- 1 tablespoon canola oil
- 1 onion, finely chopped
- 1 jalapeño chile pepper, seeded and minced (wear gloves to prevent irritation)
- 2 garlic cloves, finely chopped
- 1 pound zucchini, diced
- 2 tomatoes, seeded and diced
- ¾ cup fresh or thawed frozen corn kernels
- ½ teaspoon salt
- ⅛ teaspoon freshly ground pepper
- 2 tablespoons chopped fresh cilantro

HANDS-ON PREP 15 MIN
COOK 11 MIN
SERVES 4

Heat the oil in a large nonstick skillet over medium-high heat. Add the onion and cook, stirring occasionally, until softened, about 3 minutes. Add the jalapeño pepper and garlic; cook, stirring frequently, until fragrant, about 30 seconds. Add the zucchini and cook, stirring occasionally, until crisp-tender, about 3 minutes. Add the tomatoes, corn, salt, and ground pepper; cook, stirring occasionally, until softened, about 3 minutes. Stir in the cilantro.

PER SERVING (about ¾ cup): 98 Cal, 4 g Fat, 0 g Sat Fat, 0 g Trans Fat, 0 mg Chol, 311 mg Sod, 15 g Carb, 3 g Fib, 3 g Prot, 34 mg Calc. *POINTS* value: *2.*

☀ GOOD IDEA **While this dish may be a bit on the spicy side, it's not fiery hot. But if you like lots of heat, stir in ½ teaspoon chopped chipotle en adobo with the vegetables.**

Yuca with Garlic Sauce

2 pounds yuca, peeled,
halved lengthwise, and
cut into 2-inch chunks
4 teaspoons olive oil
3 scallions, finely chopped
3 garlic cloves, minced
½ cup vegetable or
reduced-sodium chicken
broth
1 tablespoon chopped
fresh parsley
1 tablespoon fresh lime
juice
¼ teaspoon salt
¼ teaspoon freshly ground
pepper

HANDS-ON PREP 15 MIN
COOK 30 MIN
SERVES 6

1 Combine the yuca and enough water to cover by
2 inches in a medium saucepan; bring to a boil. Reduce
the heat and cook until the yuca is very soft and
translucent, about 25 minutes. Drain; transfer to a
platter and keep warm.

2 Meanwhile, to make the garlic sauce, heat the oil in a
medium nonstick skillet over medium heat. Add the
scallions and garlic; cook, stirring constantly, until
softened, about 30 seconds. Stir in the broth and bring
to a simmer. Remove from the heat; stir in the parsley,
lime juice, salt, and pepper. Drizzle over the yuca and
serve at once.

PER SERVING (1 cup): 215 Cal, 4 g Fat, 1 g Sat Fat,
0 g Trans Fat, 0 mg Chol, 561 mg Sod, 42 g Carb, 2 g Fib,
5 g Prot, 142 mg Calc. **POINTS** value: **4.**

☀ TRY IT *Yuca* (YUHK-uh) is a starchy root
vegetable that is also called cassava. It looks like an
elongated potato with tough brown skin. It can be
stored in a cool, dry place up to 4 days. Yuca is
available in supermarkets and most Hispanic
markets. If you can't find it, substitute an equal
amount of all-purpose potatoes.

HOW-TO'S

Roasted vegetables and freshly ground seeds, nuts, herbs, and spices are some of the elements that give south-of-the-border food its rich flavor.

TO ROAST TOMATOES Core firm-ripe tomatoes and halve. Preheat the broiler and line the broiler rack with foil. Place the tomatoes, cut side down, on the rack and broil 4 to 6 inches from the heat until charred and blistered. Turn the tomatoes over and broil until lightly charred.

TO ROAST TOMATILLOS Remove the husks from fresh tomatillos and wash them well. Preheat the broiler and line the broiler rack with foil. Place the tomatillos on the rack and broil 4 to 6 inches from the heat, turning, until lightly charred on all sides.

TO ROAST FRESH CHILE PEPPERS Preheat the broiler and line the broiler rack with foil. Place the chiles on the rack and broil 4 to 6 inches from the heat, turning, until lightly charred on all sides. When the chiles are cool enough to handle and wearing rubber gloves to prevent irritation, peel, seed, and devein the chiles.

TO GRIND SEEDS, NUTS, HERBS, AND SPICES A mini-food processor or electric coffee grinder is the best tool for making seasoning pastes and spice mixtures. Or use a mortar and pestle, if you prefer. Be sure to clean the machines well with a damp paper towel after each use.

Roasted Peppers with Salsa Criolla

3 large green bell peppers
3 large yellow or orange
  bell peppers
3 tomatoes, chopped
⅓ cup chopped onion
2 tablespoons chopped
  fresh flat-leaf parsley
1 tablespoon extra-virgin
  olive oil
1 tablespoon red-wine
  vinegar
1 garlic clove, crushed
  through a press
¼ teaspoon salt
¼ teaspoon freshly ground
  pepper

HANDS-ON PREP 12 MIN
COOK 15 MIN
SERVES 6

1 Preheat the broiler. Line a baking sheet with foil and place the bell peppers on it. Broil 5 inches from the heat, turning frequently with tongs, until blackened all over, about 10 minutes. Wrap the peppers in the foil and let steam about 10 minutes. When the peppers are cool enough to handle, peel, remove the seeds, and coarsely chop. Arrange on a platter.

2 Combine the tomatoes, onion, parsley, oil, vinegar, garlic, salt, and ground pepper in a medium bowl. Spoon the salsa over the bell peppers.

PER SERVING (½ cup bell peppers and ½ cup salsa): 78 Cal, 3 g Fat, 0 g Sat Fat, 0 g Trans Fat, 0 mg Chol, 107 mg Sod, 13 g Carb, 3 g Fib, 2 g Prot, 30 mg Calc. **POINTS** value: **1.**

✹ GOOD IDEA **In Mexico,** *salsa criolla* **(fresh tomato sauce) is often served with grilled meat, but we think it also makes a great topping for roasted bell peppers. To make this dish ahead, cover and refrigerate the roasted peppers and the salsa separately overnight, then assemble the dish and allow it to come to room temperature before serving.**

Avocado with Salsa Cruda

4 plum tomatoes, diced
½ green bell pepper, seeded
   and chopped
½ cup finely chopped onion
1 tablespoon red-wine
   vinegar
¼ teaspoon salt
⅛ teaspoon freshly ground
   pepper
2 small Hass avocados,
   halved, pitted, and peeled

HANDS-ON PREP 12 MIN
COOK NONE
SERVES 8

1 Combine the tomatoes, bell pepper, onion, vinegar, salt, and ground pepper in a medium bowl.

2 Cut each avocado half lengthwise into quarters. Serve with the salsa.

PER SERVING (2 pieces avocado and ⅓ cup salsa): 70 Cal, 5 g Fat, 1 g Sat Fat, 0 g Trans Fat, 0 mg Chol, 78 mg Sod, 6 g Carb, 3 g Fib, 1 g Prot, 10 mg Calc. **POINTS** value: *1.*

☼ **FOOD NOTE** We love the buttery and luscious Hass avocado from California for this recipe. What's the best way to tell if an avocado is ready to use? Gently squeeze the fruit in the palm of your hand. Ripe, ready-to-eat avocado will be firm yet will yield to gentle pressure.

GLAZED SWEET POTATOES
WITH CHILE SAUCE

Glazed Sweet Potatoes with Chile Sauce

4 large garlic cloves,
  unpeeled
1 (3-ounce) package dried
  ancho chile peppers
  (about 6 medium), seeded
  (wear gloves to prevent
  irritation)
1 teaspoon dried oregano
½ teaspoon cinnamon
¼ teaspoon freshly ground
  pepper
⅛ teaspoon ground cloves
½ cup water
1 tablespoon grated orange
  zest
½ cup fresh orange juice
2 tablespoons honey
¾ teaspoon salt
4 (¾-pound) sweet
  potatoes, scrubbed and
  each quartered lengthwise
Chopped fresh cilantro
  (optional)

HANDS-ON PREP 20 MIN
COOK 1 HR
SERVES 8

1 Heat a large heavy skillet over medium heat. Add the garlic to one side of the skillet and cook, turning occasionally, until soft and blackened in spots, 10–12 minutes. Transfer to a plate. When cool enough to handle, peel the garlic.

2 Meanwhile, open 1 or 2 of the ancho chiles flat. Place them in the skillet in a single layer and press down firmly with a spatula. Toast until crackly and just beginning to smoke, about 20 seconds on each side. Transfer the chiles to a small bowl. Repeat with the remaining peppers. Add enough hot water to cover the chiles. Let stand, stirring occasionally, until hydrated, about 25 minutes. Drain and discard the liquid.

3 Put the chiles, garlic, oregano, cinnamon, ground pepper, cloves, and water in a food processor or blender and puree. Strain the chile mixture through a fine sieve into a small bowl. Stir in the orange zest and juice, honey, and salt.

4 Meanwhile, preheat the oven to 350°F. Spray a 9 x 13-inch baking dish with nonstick spray.

5 Place the potatoes, cut side up, in the dish in a single layer. Spoon the chile mixture evenly on top. Cover the dish tightly with foil and bake until the potatoes are fork-tender, about 45 minutes. Sprinkle with cilantro, if using.

Per serving (2 slices potato): 191 Cal, 0 g Fat, 0 g Sat Fat, 0 g Trans Fat, 0 mg Chol, 285 mg Sod, 45 g Carb, 6 g Fib, 4 g Prot, 80 mg Calc. **POINTS** value: **3.**

Sweet Treats
and Beverages

CHAPTER 9

CINNAMON FLAN

Cinnamon Flan

1 cup sugar
½ cup water
2¼ cups low-fat (1%) milk
¾ cup fat-free sweetened condensed milk
2 (3-inch) cinnamon sticks
1 teaspoon vanilla extract
1 (1-inch-wide) strip orange peel
4 large eggs, lightly beaten
1 egg white, lightly beaten

HANDS-ON PREP 15 MIN
COOK 1 HOUR 15 MIN
SERVES 8

1 Arrange a rack in the middle of the oven. Preheat the oven to 350°F.

2 Combine the sugar and water in a medium heavy-bottomed saucepan. Bring to a boil over medium-high heat; cook, shaking the pan occasionally, until golden, 12–15 minutes. Immediately pour the caramel into a 9-inch deep-dish glass pie plate; tilt the pan to evenly coat. Set aside until cool and hard, 8–10 minutes.

3 Meanwhile, combine the low-fat milk, condensed milk, cinnamon sticks, vanilla, and orange peel in a saucepan. Cook over medium heat, stirring, until almost simmering. Remove from the heat; let stand 15 minutes. Remove the cinnamon and peel. Beat the eggs and egg white in a bowl. Whisk in the milk mixture until combined. Pour into the pie plate.

4 Set the flan in a roasting pan and fill with enough hot water to come halfway up the side of the pie plate. Bake until the custard is set but jiggles in the center, 50–55 minutes. Transfer to a rack; let cool 1 hour. Refrigerate the flan for at least 3 hours. To unmold, run the tip of a knife around the edge of the flan. Invert a large, flat plate on top of the flan and flip it over. Lift off the pie plate. Cut the flan into wedges and serve.

PER SERVING (⅛ of pudding): 248 Cal, 3 g Fat, 1 g Sat Fat, 0 g Trans Fat, 110 mg Chol, 96 mg Sod, 47 g Carb, 0 g Fib, 8 g Prot, 178 mg Calc. **POINTS** value: **5.**

Butter and Sugar–Glazed Plantains

2 tablespoons unsalted butter
2 very ripe plantains, peeled and cut on diagonal into ¼-inch-thick slices
1 tablespoon sugar
1 tablespoon fresh lemon juice
¼ teaspoon almond extract
2 cups vanilla fat-free frozen yogurt

HANDS-ON PREP 5 MIN
COOK 10 MIN
SERVES 6

1 Melt the butter in a medium nonstick skillet over medium heat. Add the plantains and sugar; cook, turning occasionally, until browned, 7–9 minutes. Add the lemon juice and almond extract; cook until almost evaporated, about 1 minute.

2 Spoon ⅓ cup frozen yogurt into each of 4 bowls and top evenly with the plantain mixture (about ⅓ cup).

PER SERVING (1 dish): 208 Cal, 4 g Fat, 3 g Sat Fat, 0 g Trans Fat, 12 mg Chol, 52 mg Sod, 43 g Carb, 2 g Fib, 3 g Prot, 109 mg Calc. *POINTS* value: *4.*

✸ HOW WE DID IT *Maduros* (Mah-DOOR-os) is the Spanish word for "plantains," a hard, starchy cooking banana that is a staple in tropical areas. In Peru, maduros are deep fried and often served as a side dish. We've lightened the classic preparation by sautéing the plantains, then adding a touch of sugar and a generous amount of frozen yogurt, which turns the plantains into a delectable dessert.

BUTTER AND SUGAR–GLAZED PLANTAINS

ORANGE BUNDT CAKE

Orange Bundt Cake

3 large oranges, peeled,
  sectioned, and chopped
1¼ cups granulated sugar
⅓ cup water
3 cups all-purpose flour
1 cup packed dark
  brown sugar
1 teaspoon baking soda
¼ teaspoon salt
½ cup canola oil
4 large eggs
¾ cup fat-free milk
1½ tablespoons grated
  orange zest
1 teaspoon orange extract

HANDS-ON PREP 25 MIN
COOK 55 MIN
SERVES 24

1 Preheat the oven to 350°F. Spray a 10-inch Bundt pan with nonstick spray. Lightly dust with flour and tap out the excess.

2 Put the oranges in a medium bowl. Combine ¼ cup of the granulated sugar and the water in a small saucepan. Bring to a boil over medium-high heat; cook, stirring, until the sugar is dissolved, about 1 minute. Pour the syrup over the oranges; let stand at room temperature at least 3 hours or refrigerate overnight.

3 Whisk together the flour, brown sugar, the remaining 1 cup granulated sugar, the baking soda, and salt. With an electric mixer on low speed, add the remaining ingredients; beat about 3 minutes. Pour into the pan and spread evenly. Bake until a toothpick inserted into the center of the cake comes out clean, 50–55 minutes. Let cool in the pan on a rack about 15 minutes.

4 Remove the cake from the pan and let cool completely on the rack. Cut into 24 slices and serve topped with a little of the oranges and their syrup.

PER SERVING (1 slice of cake with 1 tablespoon oranges and syrup): 199 Cal, 6 g Fat, 1 g Sat Fat, 0 g Trans Fat, 35 mg Chol, 95 mg Sod, 34 g Carb, 1 g Fib, 3 g Prot, 34 mg Calc. *POINTS* value: *4.*

✸ GOOD IDEA **Feel free to substitute chopped mango and pineapple to add tropical flair, or use a favorite fruit combination.**

Almond Meringues

¾ **cup sliced blanched**
  almonds
4 **egg whites, at room**
  temperature
¼ **teaspoon cream of tartar**
1 **cup sugar**
¼ **teaspoon almond extract**

HANDS-ON PREP 20 MIN
COOK 1 HR 8 MIN
MAKES 72 COOKIES

1 Preheat the oven to 350°F. Line a large baking sheet with foil.

2 Heat a dry medium skillet over medium heat. Add the almonds and cook, shaking the pan occasionally, until lightly browned, 6–8 minutes. Transfer to a plate and let cool completely, about 15 minutes.

3 Place the almonds in a food processor and process until finely ground, about 1 minute.

4 With an electric mixer on medium speed, beat the egg whites and cream of tartar in a medium bowl until soft peaks form. Add the sugar in a slow, steady stream, beating until stiff, glossy peaks form, about 5 minutes. Beat in the almond extract; gently fold in the almonds.

5 Transfer the egg-white mixture to a pastry bag without a tip or a large plastic bag with one corner snipped off. Pipe 72 mounds, about 1 rounded tablespoon each, onto the baking sheet, about ½ inch apart. Place the baking sheet in the oven and reduce the temperature to 250°F. Bake the meringues until lightly colored, about 1 hour. Let cool completely on the baking sheet on a rack. The meringues will crisp as they cool.

PER SERVING (2 cookies): 36 Cal, 1 g Fat, 0 g Sat Fat, 0 g Trans Fat, 0 mg Chol, 6 mg Sod, 6 g Carb, 0 g Fib, 1 g Prot, 6 mg Calc. **POINTS** value: **1.**

ALMOND MERINGUES WITH MEXICAN
HOT CHOCOLATE, PAGE 215

Caramel Bread Pudding

⅓ cup sugar

½ cup water

½ cup fat-free sweetened
condensed milk

1 teaspoon vanilla extract

¾ cup low-fat (1%) milk

3 large eggs, lightly beaten

1 egg white, lightly beaten

5 cups day-old multigrain
bread cubes

HANDS-ON PREP 15 MIN
COOK 40 MIN
SERVES 8

1 Preheat the oven to 350°F. Lightly spray an 8-inch square baking dish with nonstick spray.

2 Combine the sugar and water in a small heavy-bottomed saucepan. Bring to a boil over medium-high heat; cook, shaking the pan occasionally, until light golden, 8–10 minutes. Remove the saucepan from the heat and let cool about 2 minutes (the caramel will darken as it cools). Place the saucepan over low heat and whisk in the sweetened condensed milk. Cook, stirring, until the mixture is smooth, 2–3 minutes. Remove the saucepan from the heat and stir in the vanilla.

3 Combine the low-fat milk, eggs, and egg white in a large bowl. Slowly whisk the hot caramel mixture into the egg mixture until combined. Add the bread cubes and stir to coat. Let stand about 10 minutes. Pour the pudding mixture into the baking dish and bake until puffed and set, 25–30 minutes. Let stand about 15 minutes before serving.

PER SERVING (⅛ of pudding): 189 Cal, 3 g Fat, 1 g Sat Fat, 0 g Trans Fat, 82 mg Chol, 190 mg Sod, 33 g Carb, 2 g Fib, 7 g Prot, 110 mg Calc. *POINTS* value: **4.**

✺ HOW WE DID IT **Bakeries throughout Mexico abound with bread puddings made with caramel. Traditional versions call for *cajeta* (ka-KHEY-tah), caramel prepared with goat's milk. Here fat-free sweetened condensed milk contributes just as much creaminess and an intense caramel flavor too.**

Mexican Hot Chocolate

4 cups fat-free milk
⅓ cup packed dark brown sugar
¼ cup unsweetened cocoa powder
1 ounce semisweet chocolate, chopped
¼ teaspoon cinnamon

HANDS-ON PREP 5 MIN
COOK 5 MIN
SERVES 4

Whisk together the milk, brown sugar, cocoa, chocolate, and cinnamon in a medium saucepan until well blended. Cook over medium heat, stirring often, until the mixture is hot and the chocolate is melted, 5–6 minutes. Pour into mugs and serve at once.

PER SERVING (1 cup): 198 Cal, 3 g Fat, 2 g Sat Fat, 0 g Trans Fat, 5 mg Chol, 112 mg Sod, 37 g Carb, 2 g Fib, 10 g Prot, 333 mg Calc. *POINTS* value: *4.*

☀ EXPRESS LANE Here's a great way to have our fabulous hot chocolate ready almost instantly. Mix a batch of the dry ingredients, divide into fourths, and store each portion in a zip-close plastic bag. Then all you have to do is mix it with 1 cup fat-free milk and heat it up.

Honeydew-Mango Shake

1 mango, pitted, peeled, and cubed (about 2 cups)
2 cups honeydew melon cubes
1 cup fat-free milk
⅓ cup fat-free sweetened condensed milk
1 cup ice cubes
Fresh mint sprigs, for garnish (optional)

HANDS-ON PREP 10 MIN
COOK NONE
SERVES 4

Combine the mango, honeydew, milk, sweetened condensed milk, and ice cubes in a blender. Process until thick and smooth, 1–2 minutes. Pour into glasses and garnish with mint sprigs, if using.

PER SERVING (1 generous cup): 160 Cal, 0 g Fat, 0 g Sat Fat, 0 g Trans Fat, 2 mg Chol, 67 mg Sod, 37 g Carb, 2 g Fib, 5 g Prot, 161 mg Calc. *POINTS* value: *3.*

TRY IT *Batidos* (fruit shakes) are very popular in Cuba and throughout Latin America; they are very refreshing in the heat. For an even thicker shake, we like to freeze the fruit for a few hours prior to making the drinks.

Limeade

1 cup sugar
1 cup water
¼ cup packed fresh cilantro
  leaves
¼ cup packed fresh basil
  leaves
¼ cup packed fresh mint
  leaves
4 cups ice water
¾ cup fresh lime juice
  (about 5 limes)
Lime slices
Fresh cilantro, basil, or
  mint leaves, for garnish

HANDS-ON PREP 15 MIN
COOK 3 MIN
SERVES 6

1 Combine the sugar and water in a medium saucepan. Bring to a boil over medium-high heat; cook about 1 minute. Remove from the heat and stir in the packed cilantro, basil, and mint leaves. Let stand about 30 minutes. Strain into a large pitcher; discard the herbs.

2 Add the ice water and lime juice to the pitcher; stir well. Pour into tall ice-filled glasses, add a few lime slices to each glass, and garnish with herb leaves.

PER SERVING (1 cup): 136 Cal, 0 g Fat, 0 g Sat Fat, 0 g Trans Fat, 0 mg Chol, 10 mg Sod, 35 g Carb, 0 g Fib, 0 g Prot, 8 mg Calc. *POINTS* value: *3.*

✺ HOW WE DID IT **To get the most juice out of limes (or lemons), roll each one on the counter, pressing down with the palm of your hand. This will help release all the juice. Look for limes that have the thinnest skin, as they tend to contain more juice.**

Sangria

1 (750-ml) bottle dry
  red wine
½ cup orange juice
½ cup pineapple chunks
½ apple, cored and cubed
3 tablespoons sugar
1 tablespoon fresh lime
  juice
1 cup cold seltzer water

HANDS-ON PREP 10 MIN
COOK NONE
SERVES 6

1 Combine the wine, orange juice, pineapple, apple, sugar, and lime juice in a large pitcher; stir until the sugar is dissolved. Refrigerate at least 2 hours or up to overnight.

2 Just before serving, stir in the seltzer. Pour the sangria into 6 ice-filled glasses, being sure to include some fruit.

PER SERVING (1 cup): 135 Cal, 0 g Fat, 0 g Sat Fat, 0 g Trans Fat, 0 mg Chol, 7 mg Sod, 14 g Carb, 1 g Fib, 0 g Prot, 16 mg Calc.
POINTS value: **3.**

☼ GOOD IDEA **For a nonalcoholic version, substitute 4 cups of grape juice for the wine, omit the orange juice and sugar, and increase the seltzer to 2 cups.**

Watermelon Agua Fresca

8 cups seedless
   watermelon cubes
1 cup cold water
3 tablespoons sugar
2 tablespoons fresh lime
   juice
6 watermelon wedges, for
   garnish

HANDS-ON PREP 15 MIN
COOK NONE
SERVES 6

Combine 4 cups of the watermelon cubes and ½ cup of the water in a blender and puree. Press the mixture through a sieve set over a medium bowl. Pour into a large pitcher. Repeat with the remaining watermelon and water. Add the sugar and lime juice to the pitcher; stir until the sugar is dissolved. Pour the agua fresca into 6 ice-filled glasses. Garnish each drink with a watermelon wedge.

PER SERVING (1 cup): 75 Cal, 0 g Fat, 0 g Sat Fat, 0 g Trans Fat, 0 mg Chol, 4 mg Sod, 19 g Carb, 1 g Fib, 1 g Prot, 13 mg Calc. *POINTS* value: *1.*

✴ EXPRESS LANE At local markets throughout Mexico, there are stands that sell this refreshing fruit drink. Agua fresca can be stored in a sealed container up to 4 days in your refrigerator.

VERACRUZ-STYLE ARROZ CON POLLO, PAGE 100

Dry and Liquid Measurement Equivalents

If you are converting the recipes in this book to metric measurements, use the following chart as a guide.

TEASPOONS	TABLESPOONS	CUPS	FLUID OUNCES
3 teaspoons	1 tablespoon		1/2 fluid ounce
6 teaspoons	2 tablespoons	1/8 cup	1 fluid ounce
8 teaspoons	2 tablespoons plus 2 teaspoons	1/6 cup	
12 teaspoons	4 tablespoons	1/4 cup	2 fluid ounces
15 teaspoons	5 tablespoons	1/3 cup minus 1 teaspoon	
16 teaspoons	5 tablespoons plus 1 teaspoon	1/3 cup	
18 teaspoons	6 tablespoons	1/4 cup plus 2 tablespoons	3 fluid ounces
24 teaspoons	8 tablespoons	1/2 cup	4 fluid ounces
30 teaspoons	10 tablespoons	1/2 cup plus 2 tablespoons	5 fluid ounces
32 teaspoons	10 tablespoons plus 2 teaspoons	2/3 cup	
36 teaspoons	12 tablespoons	3/4 cup	6 fluid ounces
42 teaspoons	14 tablespoons	1 cup minus 2 tablespoons	7 fluid ounces
45 teaspoons	15 tablespoons	1 cup minus 1 tablespoon	
48 teaspoons	16 tablespoons	1 cup	8 fluid ounces

VOLUME	
1/4 teaspoon	1 milliliter
1/2 teaspoon	2 milliliters
1 teaspoon	5 milliliters
1 tablespoon	15 milliliters
2 tablespoons	30 milliliters
3 tablespoons	45 milliliters
1/4 cup	60 milliliters
1/3 cup	80 milliliters
1/2 cup	120 milliliters
2/3 cup	160 milliliters
3/4 cup	175 milliliters
1 cup	240 milliliters
1 quart	950 milliliters

OVEN TEMPERATURE

250°F	120°C	400°F	200°C
275°F	140°C	425°F	220°C
300°F	150°C	450°F	230°C
325°F	160°C	475°F	250°C
350°F	180°C	500°F	260°C
375°F	190°C	525°F	270°C

LENGTH

1 inch	25 millimeters
1 inch	2.5 centimeters

WEIGHT

1 ounce	30 grams
1/4 pound	120 grams
1/2 pound	240 grams
1 pound	480 grams

NOTE: Measurement of less than 1/8 teaspoon is considered a dash or a pinch. Metric volume measurements are approximate.

Index

POINTS value Recipe Index

5 POINTS value

Black Bean and Swiss Chard Burritos, 172

Butterflied Leg of Lamb, Santa Fe–Style, 88

Chicken with Pumpkin Seed–Tomatillo Sauce, 112

Chicken, Tomato, and Tortilla Stew, 5

Chunky Turkey Chili with Lentils, 133

Cinnamon Flan, 207

Colombian Beef and Onion Salad, 46

Cuban-Style Christmas Eve Pork Roast, 78

Easy Chicken Mole, 121

Grilled Tempeh with Tomato-Mint Salsa, 169

Hot-and-Sweet Pepper Soft Tacos, 167

Mexicali Shrimp in Pumpkin Seed Sauce, 152

Mexican Seafood Chowder, 39

Peruvian Tuna Seviche, 143

Picadillo with Tortilla Crisps, 74

Red-Roasted Chicken with Sweet Potatoes, 97

Ropa Vieja, 69

Salmon with Guacamole and Pico de Gallo, 136

Sesame-Crusted Chicken Breasts with Mango-Jicama Salsa, 110

Shredded Pork and Onion Tacos, 84

Slow-Cooked Striped Bass with Vegetables, 147

Spanish-Style Roast Leg of Lamb, 86

Spicy Bean, Tomato, and Cheese–Stuffed Zucchini, 182

Spicy Yucatán Beef Tacos, 71

Spinach, Bell Pepper, and Flank Steak Roll, 66

Turkey Posole with Radish-Scallion Topping, 34

"Unfried" Tofu Tosdadas, 165

Vegetarian Sausage and Mushroom Pilaf, 179

6 POINTS value

Apple Jelly and Chipotle–Glazed Pork Chops, 82

Brazilian Black Bean and Chorizo Soup, 37

Broiled Salmon with Chipotle Cream, 138

Carnitas Tostadas, 93

Chicken and Avocado Tacos, 113

Chicken and Pepperjack Tortilla Casserole, 131

Chicken Breasts with Bacon, Olives, and Capers, 103

Chicken Tacos with Roasted Tomato–Corn Salsa, 125

Chicken-Rice Soup with Cumin Cream, 33

Chicken-Vegetable Platter with Tomato-Salsa Dressing, 105

Chili Verde, 123

Colombian Pinto Bean Casserole, 174

Cuban Beef and Butternut Squash Stew, 72

Green Chile Picadillo, 124

Grilled Salmon with Pickled Onions, 139

Honey-Chipotle Marinated T-bone Steaks, 65

Oaxacan Chicken and Chickpea Stew, 126

Peruvian Chicken-Potato Salad, 45

Pickled Chicken and Vegetables, 104

Roasted Pepper and Chicken Quesadillas, 130

Spanish Meatballs in Sauce, 73

Tequilla Turkey with Lime and Cilantro, 132

7 POINTS value

Baked Tuna with Majoram and Lime, 140

Black Bean, Chicken, and Roasted Corn Stew, 129

Chicken and Cremini Mushroom Fajitas, 118

Classic Arroz con Pollo, 102

Enchiladas Suizas, 107

Lamb and Bell Pepper Fajitas, 91

Plantain, Raisin, and Pork Stew with Ancho Chiles, 83

Southwest Chicken, Bean, and Corn Soup, 36

Tempeh Salpicón, 166

Turkey, Black Bean, and Tomatillo Layered Salad, 48

8 POINTS value

Brazilian Shellfish with Rice, 161

Chicken with Plaintain and Stewed Tomatoes, 120

Hearty Chicken and Potato Stew, 98

Lamb and Brown Rice Burritos, 92

Pork Chops with Prunes and Red Pepper, 81

Pork with Red Mole Sauce, 76

Roasted Vegetable Enchiladas, 185

Tortilla, Beef, and Bean Soup, 31

Veracruz-Style Arroz con Pollo, 100

9 POINTS value

Spicy Pork, Sweet Potato, and Plantain Bowl, 32

Notes